MOSAICO ITALIANO
Racconti per stranieri
13

Bianca Maria Brivio

Rapito!

LIVELLO 1/4

BONACCI EDITORE

Illustrazione in copertina di Raquel Garcia Maciá

Printed in Italy

Bonacci editore
Via Paolo Mercuri, 8
00193 ROMA (Italia)
tel:(0039)06.68.30.00.04
fax:(0039)06.68.80.63.82
e-mail: info@bonacci.it
http://www.bonacci.it

PARTE 1

1
Giorno uno

Apro gli occhi. Non capisco dove mi trovo. Ma di una cosa sono sicuro: non mi trovo nella mia camera. Mi alzo in piedi con fatica e mi guardo intorno: la mia giacca è a terra. Adesso ricordo tutto. In un flash. E quei ricordi mi fanno star male come quando si sale all'ultimo piano di un grattacielo e si guarda giù...

La stanza è brutta e vuota. Non ci sono mobili: soltanto un letto. Sul pavimento vedo una bottiglia d'acqua. Prendo la bottiglia con la mano che mi trema e bevo.

Nella stanza c'è poca luce. "Perché? – mi chiedo – Non ci sono finestre?" Osservo le pareti. Sì, c'è una finestrella, ma è molto in alto e coperta da sbarre[1].

"Comunque non me ne faccio niente – dico tra me e me – È così in alto che devo salire su qualcosa per arrivarci e qui non c'è neppure una sedia!"

Vado nell'altra stanzetta. È piccolissima: ci sono soltanto un gabinetto e una pila di giornali per terra.

Sono ancora nella stanzetta quando sento dei rumori. Torno a letto e mi sdraio. Rimango immobile. Sento dei passi veloci: qualcuno è entrato nella stanza. Alzo la testa per guardare: è un uomo, ma non ne vedo la faccia. Ha una specie di maschera che la copre.

"Ti ho portato un piatto con qualcosa da mangiare, ragazzo" dice.

Esce subito, veloce e deciso, come è entrato.

Appena è fuori, mi prende una grande paura. Tremo come una foglia. Cerco di pensare, ma non ci riesco. Continuo a tremare e penso. O forse... sogno?

È una giornata di sole. Fa caldo anche se è già ottobre.

Il campo di calcio è grande, forse anche troppo grande per le due squadrette.

La palla corre corre e sembra legata ai piedi di questo e quello. Poi la prendo io. Corro, mi scontro con un giocatore dell'altra squadra, inseguo ancora la palla e faccio gol. È un grande gol. Il primo della mia vita. I miei compagni di squadra saltano e gridano.

---

[1] *sbarre:* si usano per proteggere le finestre.

3

Io sono contento ed emozionato! Ho molta sete. Vado a bere alla fontanella appena fuori dal campo. Mentre bevo sento ancora le voci dei miei compagni di squadra: "Bravo Riccardo, sei stato un grande!", "Vai Riccardo..."

Sorrido. Sento una mano sulla spalla.

"Questo deve essere Max" penso. Ma non faccio in tempo a voltarmi. La stessa mano mi afferra[2] con forza.

Grido, ma la mano non mi lascia; anzi, un'altra mano mi afferra da dietro.

Sollevo la testa. E vedo una scena da film dell'orrore: due individui mi stanno davanti e hanno delle maschere sulla faccia.

Poi mi mettono qualcosa sulla bocca e sento un sapore terribile.

Cado nel buio. Il mio ultimo pensiero: "Sono morto."

Mi sveglio di colpo. Il cuore mi batte forte nel petto. Sto seduto sul letto nella stanza buia.

"Mio Dio, mio Dio – penso – non è un sogno, non è stato un sogno."

Tremo di nuovo.

"Smettila di tremare – mi dico arrabbiato – è inutile. Cerca di riflettere invece."

Cerco la bottiglia con le mani. La prendo e bevo. Ho sempre tanta sete. Quando metto la bottiglia per terra, tocco un oggetto: è un piatto.

"È vero. – penso – Quell'uomo ha portato qualcosa da mangiare. Lo avevo dimenticato!"

Non ho fame, ma mangio lo stesso. Sono tre fette di prosciutto cotto con un panino. Poi bevo ancora. Adesso mi sento meglio. Il cibo mi ha dato un po' di forza.

Vado verso la porta e ci incollo[3] l'orecchio: niente, non si sente niente di niente, non il più piccolo rumore.

Adesso non sono più stanco, non ho voglia di dormire; comincio a camminare avanti e indietro. I miei piedi vanno su e giù per la stanza: e intanto la mia mente fa *tic tac tic tac* al ritmo dei miei passi.

Qualcuno mi ha rapito; due persone, forse di più. Perché? Per chiedere un riscatto, naturalmente. Perché hanno rapito proprio *me*? I miei genitori sono ricchi? Credo di sì. La mia casa è molto bella e molto grande: per me è una casa normale ma, se penso a dove vivono i miei amici... per esempio Max. Lui abita in un appartamento con tre stanze.

---

[2] *afferra:* prende.

[3] *ci incollo:* metto molto vicino, aderente a…

Non ha cuoca né cameriera, nel giardino non ci sono piscina né campo da tennis. La mia casa, invece, ha più di venti stanze e nel giardino ci sono la piscina e il campo da tennis.

Mi fermo un attimo. Ho visto un piccolo topo. Si muove. Lo inseguo, ma lui è più veloce e scappa verso un angolo. Non lo vedo più.

Ricomincio a camminare. Avanti e indietro, avanti e indietro.

Torno ai miei pensieri: quindi mi hanno rapito per avere soldi dai miei genitori. Quanti soldi? Non riesco a immaginarlo. Ma la domanda più importante è: i miei genitori possono pagare?

Di nuovo una domanda senza risposta…

Sono stanco di camminare e mi siedo sul letto.

"Non posso passare tutto il tempo così – mi dico – devo fare qualcosa." Ma… che cosa? Non c'è niente in questa stanza.

2
I giornali

In questa stanza non c'è niente, ma nell'altra?

"Lì ho visto qualcosa… – penso – La pila di giornali!"

Mi siedo per terra e li guardo uno a uno. Sono giornali vecchi, ma che importa? L'importante è fare qualcosa.

Prendo il primo. Non leggo le pagine di politica, la politica non m'interessa.

Mi piacciono invece gli articoli di cronaca nera e spettacolo[4].

Sono ancora seduto a leggere quando sento la porta che si apre. Salto in piedi e vado nell'altra stanza. È l'uomo con la maschera. In mano tiene una macchina fotografica.

"Dov'eri?" chiede con voce cattiva.

"In bagno."

"Siediti adesso!" mi dice.

Io mi siedo e lui rimane in piedi davanti a me.

"Devo sorridere?" chiedo.

Sembra una battuta[5], ma non lo è. Non so perché l'ho detta.

---

[4] *cronaca nera e spettacolo:* la cronaca nera riguarda delitti e crimini vari, le pagine relative allo spettacolo, invece, trattano di spettacoli teatrali.

[5] *battuta:* scherzo.

5

L'uomo fa un passo verso di me e mi dà un ceffone[6] in faccia. È così forte che quasi cado.

Mi viene da piangere. Ma non voglio. Non mi deve vedere piangere. E non piango.

"Guarda verso di me" dice l'uomo.

Tre volte un flash illumina la stanza, poi l'uomo va verso la porta. Non dice niente, esce e basta. La porta si chiude.

Io torno nella stanzetta e ricomincio a leggere, ma non per molto.

A poco a poco la luce va via.

"Viene la sera. – penso – Devono essere le sei e mezzo. A quest'ora fa buio."

Non so cosa fare, vado a letto. Sono stanco anche se non ho fatto niente. Mi addormento.

Quando mi sveglio, è mattina. Lo capisco perché la luce entra dalla finestrella.

Mi alzo e in quel momento sento il rumore della chiave. È l'uomo. Porta qualcosa in mano.

"La colazione" dice.

Ha una voce fredda e metallica come quella del mio computer.

"Signore, signore… posso chiederle una cosa?" domando io.

L'uomo mi guarda, ma non parla.

"La prego, signore, mi dica… Perché mi tenete qui?"

"Se non l'hai capito sei un vero idiota, ragazzo."

Va verso la porta. Io lo seguo.

"Signore" domando ancora" hanno pagato il riscatto?"

Nessuna risposta.

La porta si richiude. Ha lasciato un sacchetto, la mia "colazione". È un sacchetto[7] di una panetteria. C'è dentro una brioche. Buonissima. Con crema di cioccolato, la mia preferita. Guardo il sacchetto: il nome del panettiere è Stelladi. Non lo conosco. Nel sacchetto trovo anche una bottiglia, in plastica, di latte. Lo bevo. Sto bene adesso. Rimango ancora un po' sdraiato, poi torno ai miei giornali.

In un vecchio numero del novembre 1998 leggo un articolo su un ragazzo. Anche lui rapito.

---

[6] *ceffone*: sberla, schiaffo.

[7] *sacchetto*: nel nord Italia si intende una busta di plastica mentre nel centro sud si intende una bustina di carta.

Il ragazzo ha quindici anni, come me. Il suo nome è Giannetto e abita a Napoli. Rapito davanti a casa, lo tengono rinchiuso per tre settimane in una baracca al buio. Anche i suoi rapitori sono mascherati e lui non li vede mai in faccia.

Alla fine lo liberano. La famiglia paga il riscatto e lui torna a casa. Ai giornalisti dice soltanto una frase: "Ero disperato. Ho avuto così tanta paura…"

"Anche tu sei disperato, anche tu hai paura" dice una vocetta dentro di me. Ma io non l'ascolto e continuo a leggere. Anche se sono stanco. Ma se non leggo, penso e non voglio pensare.

Sento che l'uomo sta entrando. Mi alzo e torno in camera.

L'uomo prende il sacchetto della colazione e la bottiglia di latte, vuota. Mi dà un altro sacchetto e una bottiglia d'acqua.

"Per oggi" dice. Poi esce.

Mangio tutto subito. Però alla fine mi fa un po' male lo stomaco.

"Forse è perché non mangio niente di caldo" mi dico.

Sento la voce di mia mamma: "Almeno un pasto caldo al giorno è necessario."

Mia mamma, la mia famiglia…

"Chissà cosa stanno facendo adesso?" mi chiedo." Forse stanno aspettando la telefonata dei rapitori?"

Devono essere tutti nel grande soggiorno della casa. Mamma, papà, Betta… C'è anche la polizia? Credo di sì. I miei compagni e i genitori al campo di calcio forse hanno visto gli uomini con la maschera e hanno chiamato la polizia. Senz'altro c'è mio fratello Filippo. È lì con i miei genitori perché non è andato a scuola. Per Filippo ogni scusa è buona per non andare a scuola. Chissà se è preoccupato anche lui? In effetti noi due non andiamo per niente d'accordo. Litighiamo spesso. Forse perché ha cinque anni meno di me e siamo così diversi. Forse lui è contento se non torno più a casa. Non torno più a casa… che cosa terribile! Non ci devo pensare.

E Betta? Lei è sicuramente preoccupata. Betta è come una seconda mamma per me.

"Adesso però devo fare qualcosa" mi dico.

Cammino per le due stanze. Guardo la porta. Che cosa può esserci oltre quella porta? Quando l'uomo esce, vedo sempre un corridoio. Ci sono altre stanze?

Oppure mi trovo in una cantina? Non lo so.

Guardo la finestrella. È così in alto… Come posso arrivarci, senza sedie né altro?

Improvvisamente mi viene un'idea.

3
Il barbone

Se sto in piedi sul letto posso guardare fuori. Posso portare il letto fino alla finestrella!

L'operazione sembra semplice, ma mi costa una grande fatica. Il letto è molto pesante e io sono debole. A ogni piccolo rumore mi fermo perché ho paura dell'uomo mascherato.

Finalmente sono con il letto sotto la finestrella. Vado in bagno, prendo la pila di giornali, li metto sul letto e salgo. Sìì, ce l'ho fatta. Riesco a guardare fuori. Ma cosa vedo? Praticamente niente! Soltanto uno spazio grigio, forse un cortile[8]. Sulla destra deve esserci una strada perché da lì sento venire il rumore delle automobili.

Sono deluso. Quella era la mia ultima speranza…

Rimango lì in piedi per dieci, quindici minuti. Cerco qualcosa in quello spazio grigio, ma non vedo niente se non due bidoni della spazzatura.

Adesso sta venendo sera. È quasi buio. Rimetto il letto al suo posto.

Ho tanta fame. Ho una grande voglia di mangiare qualcosa, per esempio un hamburger caldo. Lo vedo davanti a me, in un grosso panino. Mmmm, che buono… E mi viene ancora più fame.

"Basta, smettila" dico ad alta voce "così ti fai del male!"

Adesso non penso più all'hamburger e alla fame. Ma a me. Quanto ancora devo stare in questa prigione? Cosa mi può succedere? Mi sento disperato.

E piango. Per la prima volta da quando sono qui, piango.

Mi addormento molto tardi.

Quando mi sveglio, la prima cosa che sento è la fame. Lo stomaco è vuoto e mi fa male la testa. Per terra ci sono un sacchetto e una bottiglia di latte. È venuto l'uomo, ma io non l'ho sentito. Mangio la solita brioche e bevo il latte. Troppo velocemente. Ho ancora fame.

---

[8] *cortile:* area/spazio vicino a edifici che serve per il passaggio di persone, auto o altro.

Vado nella stanza da bagno e comincio a leggere i giornali. Leggo gli articoli che non ho letto prima, leggo tutto. Però non li trovo interessanti e non mi concentro. Penso ad altro. Penso a Max.

Max è il mio miglior amico, un tipo strano. Si veste sempre di nero, è molto popolare tra i ragazzi, meno popolare tra i genitori, perché tutti sanno che pensa tanto alle ragazze e poco alla scuola.

Forse Max adesso è a casa mia. No, no… a mia mamma Max non piace. Probabilmente non ha parlato con lui. Forse invece è solo *vicino* a casa mia e sta guardando il giardino pieno di macchine della polizia e di giornalisti.

Poi torna a casa e vede la televisione. Max vede tanto la televisione.

A me invece la televisione non piace molto. Però adesso… oh, come vorrei un televisore…

Via anche questo pensiero! Non devo desiderare quello che non posso avere. Mi fa stare male e basta.

Oggi c'è il sole. Vedo una forte luce che viene dalla finestrella. Sollevo lo sguardo⁹. E vedo… la faccia di un uomo! Sta guardando nella stanza. Comincio a saltare e agito le mani come un matto. Ma l'uomo va via.

Forse mi ha visto. Riporto subito il letto sotto la finestrella e metto i giornali sul letto. Sto lì in piedi per tanto tempo: un'ora, forse due ore. Ma tutto quello che vedo è il cortile grigio.

"Conto ancora fino a sessanta!" mi dico "e poi scendo."

Proprio in quel momento compare di nuovo la faccia. Come per magia. Con la bocca vicinissima al vetro a voce bassa, dico lentamente:

"Aiutami aiutami aiutami ". L'uomo, nello stesso modo, domanda:

"Perché? Cosa succede?" E io: "Rapito. Rapito. Rapito." Ripeto quella parola nove, dieci volte.

L'uomo fa sì con la testa e va via.

Porto il letto nell'angolo.

Dopo qualche minuto si apre la porta ed entra il mio rapitore. Mi dà due panini e due mele.

"Ti devono bastare fino a domani" dice.

"Da quanti giorni sono qui?" chiedo.

"Da tre giorni" risponde lui "oggi è il quarto."

Esce e chiude la porta.

---

⁹ *sollevo lo sguardo*: guardo.

Mangio una mela e un panino; tengo l'altra mela e il secondo panino per la sera. Anche se ho tanta fame.

Penso all'uomo alla finestra. Aveva un aspetto strano. I capelli lunghi, la barba grigia...

"Deve essere un barbone" mi dico. "Chissà se ha chiamato la polizia..." Ricordo cosa dice papà sui barboni: "Sono persone che non hanno niente, vivono fuori dalla società. A loro non importa di nessuno."

Se è così, allora il "mio" barbone non ha chiamato la polizia ...

Continuo a pensare e parlo ad alta voce. Parlo sempre più spesso ad alta voce. Forse sto impazzendo. Invece devo stare calmo.

Oh Dio, Dio aiutami. Mi metto seduto sul letto e prego. Prego e prego.

È notte e poi di nuovo mattina. Il quinto giorno.

Aspetto tutta la mattina e tutto il pomeriggio, ma l'uomo mascherato non viene.

Sto tutto il tempo sul letto, solo qualche volta mi alzo e cammino avanti e indietro. Però faccio tanta fatica. Quando mi sdraio penso e sogno a occhi aperti.

Quando arriva la polizia, dormo. O almeno credo. Ho fame e freddo. Non capisco bene cosa succede. Mi portano fuori, salgo in macchina. Non parlo, non dico niente. Forse, come Giannetto, sono in "stato di shock".

4
Due mesi dopo

Tutt'intorno è buio e c'è tanto silenzio. Ho paura ad aprire gli occhi e sto a letto. Sono di nuovo lì, di nuovo solo nella mia prigione. Se apro gli occhi, vedo la porta. Si sta aprendo: adesso entra l'uomo mascherato e io grido "aiuto, aiuto, aiuto!"

Invece quando apro gli occhi vedo mia mamma. Mi prende la mano nella sua.

"Hai fatto di nuovo quel brutto sogno, vero?" mi chiede. "Non devi più avere paura. È tutto finito adesso."

Io guardo intorno: sono nella mia camera.

"Lo so mamma. Ma il mio sogno sembra vero…"

"Lo so, Riccardo. Spesso i sogni sembrano veri. Ma adesso vestiti! È mattina. È ora di andare a scuola."

"Mi accompagna il papà[10] anche stamattina?" domando.

"Sì, è meglio."

"Non posso andare da solo? La scuola è molto vicina."

Non mi piace andare con papà. Parla poco, pensa sempre ai fatti suoi, forse al suo lavoro. Papà infatti lavora tanto, tutto il giorno e spesso anche di sera.

"Magari dalla prossima settimana… Adesso vestiti, dai! Altrimenti fai tardi."

Sta per uscire, quando si ferma sulla porta e mi dice:

"Riccardo, non è che forse ci hai ripensato? A proposito della psicologa, voglio dire."

"No, non ci ho ripensato. Non voglio parlare con nessuno. "

Mi lavo e mi vesto mentre penso a quello che ha detto la mamma. La psicologa… non voglio parlare con la psicologa della polizia. Ho già parlato con lei. Il giorno dopo la mia liberazione.

Ricordo bene tutto: le pareti bianche da ospedale, lei che mi guarda in silenzio, io che ho voglia di piangere perché il silenzio ormai mi spaventa.

---

[10] *il papà:* nel Nord Italia si usa molto spesso l'articolo davanti ai nomi di persona e davanti a "mamma" e "papà".

"Raccontami, Riccardo" mi dice e fa una faccia triste come me. Ma lei non è triste, non è stata come me in prigione per cinque giorni, lei non può capire. Così non le racconto niente e dopo mezz'ora me ne vado. A casa faccio la mia vita di sempre. Parlo poco di quei giorni nella prigione e i miei genitori non chiedono. Forse pensano che è meglio dimenticare e basta.

Io però conosco tutta la storia, che ho letto sui giornali: il riscatto di un milione di euro, i cinque giorni necessari per raccogliere i soldi (mio padre non è così ricco), la consegna dei soldi ai rapitori e l'arrivo della polizia, grazie ad una telefonata anonima: "C'è un ragazzo rapito in una cantina in via dei Cerberi"... una via che è solo a 10 minuti da casa mia!

Alle sette e mezzo sono pronto. Faccio colazione e poi esco di casa. In strada mi aspetta papà in macchina.

"Tuo fratello?" domanda.

"Ah, non lo so..." rispondo io. "Filippo è sempre in ritardo!"

Ecco che arriva con Betta dietro che gli grida: "Muoviti, muoviti!"

È buffo Filippo. Quando sono tornato, mi ha detto che "mi vuole bene". Anch'io gli voglio bene. Però non andiamo d'accordo e non passiamo mai tempo insieme. È così... bambino!

Nei primi giorni a scuola dopo la liberazione sono un vero vip. Tutti mi parlano. Le ragazze mi guardano come di solito guardano solo i ragazzi della quinta, i professori mi parlano con dolcezza, i miei compagni di classe sono contenti di avermi con loro.

Prima ero il solito bravo ragazzo, ma niente di più. Adesso sono al centro dell'attenzione.

"Ci si sente importante anche se non lo si è" dico a Max.

Ma anche quel momento è passato e dopo non più di una settimana sono un ragazzo come tutti gli altri. La vita è come prima. Però io non sono tornato totalmente tranquillo. Perché ho sempre un po' di paura. È lì, in un angolino del mio cuore, pronta a uscire in ogni momento.

5
Al museo

È un lunedì mattina di un freddo gennaio. Questa è la prima gita dell'anno scolastico. Andiamo in autobus al museo.

Siamo allegri, non certo per l'argomento della mostra (qualcosa sulla matematica!), ma perché non siamo a scuola.

Io sto seduto in autobus accanto a Max che parla tutto il tempo:

"Ho visto una ragazza che mi piace. È della seconda B. È bellissima. E anche la sua amica non è male."

Fino al museo non parla d'altro.

"Max" gli dico io "ma hai in testa solo le donne!"

"Non è vero" risponde lui. "Anche le… ragazze!" E ride.

Io guardo fuori dal finestrino e vedo che l'autobus passa vicino alla strada della mia prigione: via dei Cerberi.

Max mi tocca il braccio.

"Ehi, Ricky. Ti ho chiesto una cosa…"

"Ah scusa, Max…"

"Vuoi conoscere l'amica di Elisa? Si chiama Romina. Bel nome, vero?"

"Sì, è un bel nome" rispondo io per farlo contento.

Cinque minuti e siamo nella piazza di fronte al museo. Io e Max scendiamo per ultimi. Faccio qualche passo e *lo* vedo. È l'uomo che ho visto dalla finestra nella cantina. Sta guardando in uno dei bidoni della spazzatura.

"Guarda! È lui!" grido prendendo il braccio di Max.

"Lui chi?"

"Il barbone, l'uomo della cantina."

"Ma come fai a dirlo?"

"Ti dico che è lui! Ne sono sicuro!"

"Ragazzi, ragazzi, muovetevi!" ci chiama la professoressa spazientita. Mi avvicino all'uomo.

"Signore, signore!" dico, "mi riconosce? Io sono…"

Non finisco la frase perché l'uomo corre via. L'insegnante mi ha sentito alzare la voce. Viene verso di noi.

"Che cosa succede?" domanda allarmata.

"Niente, prof[11]" risponde Max "solo un ratto. È saltato fuori dal bidone della spazzatura."

"Oh, ma che schifo!"

Entriamo tutti nel museo, però io continuo a pensare all'uomo che ho visto.

---

[11] *prof:* abbreviazione di "professoressa".

Non ne parlo con nessuno se non con Max naturalmente.

"Questo sta diventando per te un chiodo fisso[12]" mi dice lui. "Che cosa vuoi fare?"

"Voglio trovarlo."

"Ma come? I tuoi non ti lasciano neanche fare tre passi in giardino da solo."

"Infatti" rispondo io e lo guardo.

"Perché mi guardi così? Non pensare che io…"

"Dai, Max…"

"Dai cosa? Cosa devo fare? Andare per la città a cercare il tuo barbone?"

"Beh, non proprio tu, magari tuo cugino."

"Ah, è questo che hai in mente. Tu pensi: il cuginetto di Max è uno che va in giro anche di notte, conosce tanta gente anche i barboni e i criminali di questa città. Io devo parlargli e lui fa tutto quello che voglio."

"Perché ti arrabbi?"

"Perché mi arrabbio… Tu cosa credi? Tu hai tanti soldi, e tutti devono fare quello che vuoi tu."

"Oh, Max! Io non ho detto proprio niente."

"Ma era questa la tua idea!"

"La mia idea era di chiedere a tuo cugino se …"

"Vedi che ho ragione!"

"Su che cosa?"

"Vai al diavolo!" grida lui e va via.

Io non lo richiamo. Sono anch'io molto arrabbiato: di nuovo la storia con i miei soldi! E ancora una volta, come quando ero prigioniero, desidero essere uno come tutti gli altri, con il papà impiegato e la mamma casalinga, uno che abita in un appartamentino in periferia. I miei soldi non mi portano niente di buono, solo problemi!

Passano due giorni. Sono triste e silenzioso: senza Max a scuola mi sento solo. È l'unico amico che ho nella mia classe. Non è facile per me fare amicizia… Sono troppo chiuso, spesso imbarazzato con gli altri.

Però non è vero che Max è l'unico amico in classe. In effetti ho un'altra amica, o quasi amica. Si chiama Sibilla, è bella, anzi bellissima, con i lunghi capelli neri e gli occhi grandi. Mi ha mandato almeno dieci sms[13]

---

[12] *sta diventando per te un chiodo fisso:* non pensi ad altro.

[13] *sms:* messaggi telefonici.

da quando sono a casa. A scuola parla sempre con me.

Oggi, dopo il litigio con Max, passo l'intervallo con lei.

"Mi leggi il tuo tema sui ricordi?" mi chiede.

"Sì, certo" rispondo io e lo leggo.

"Scrivi bene" mi dice lei. "Come un vero scrittore."

Mi sento orgoglioso come non lo sono mai stato. Tanti insegnanti mi hanno detto che scrivo bene, ma mai una ragazza carina come Sibilla.

"Grazie" rispondo, e non trovo niente di meglio da dire.

Sibilla mi guarda negli occhi e mi domanda:

"Dunque Ricky, è proprio come hai scritto? I ricordi per te sono un... tormento?"

"No... non i ricordi" rispondo. "Gli incubi sono un tormento, ma adesso ne ho di meno."

"Sogni quello che ti è successo quando eri là, prigioniero...?"

"Beh, sì, più o meno. Però non è quello che sogno, è quello che sento nel sogno. Quello è terribile."

Lei non dice niente e mi sorride.

Alla fine delle lezioni mi aspetta fuori dalla classe.

"Fai un pezzo di strada con me?" domanda.

"Mi dispiace" rispondo. "C'è mio padre fuori. Mi accompagna sempre lui a casa in macchina."

Lei sembra delusa, ma poi di nuovo sorride con il suo bel sorriso allegro.

"Non importa" dice "ci vediamo domani."

"A domani" faccio io. E dentro di me penso: "Quanto è bella e dolce..."

6
L'identikit[14]

Oggi è venerdì. Non so perché, ma mi sento felice. Forse è il pensiero di incontrare Sibilla! Invece la prima persona che vedo è Max.

In classe, prima dell'inizio delle lezioni, mi dice:

"Ehi Ricky, mi dispiace per l'altro giorno. Scusami."

"È tutto OK. Non c'è problema."

Sono sincero. In effetti non sono più arrabbiato.

---

[14] *identikit:* disegno di una persona che serve per svolgere indagini di polizia.

"Ho pensato a quello che mi hai detto – continua Max – e ti voglio aiutare."

Ma anch'io ci ho pensato e dico:

"È troppo difficile. Anzi mi sembra una cosa impossibile. Come si fa a trovare un uomo in una città come questa? Sono duecentomila abitanti e…"

"No, ascolta! Ho parlato con mio cugino Alfredo. Ha detto che si può fare. Soltanto che… "

"Che?"

"Vuole soldi."

"Beh, è giusto. Dopo tutto…"

"Dopo tutto?"

"Se uno lavora, è giusto pagarlo. Non credi?"

"Sì, hai ragione."

"Quanto vuole?"

"Dice che per trecento euro te lo trova in un paio di giorni."

"Trecento? Accidenti, trecento euro non sono pochi. Ma io non ho trec… No aspetta! Mia zia mi ha regalato cinquecento euro per il compleanno. Li ho ancora e…"

Non riesco a finire la frase. È entrata l'insegnante di inglese, che sta gridando come un'aquila: "Please, sit down please!"

Max va al suo posto.

All'intervallo continuiamo.

"A quando?" chiedo.

"Appena hai i soldi."

"OK. Allora oggi."

"Hai fretta, eh…"

Fretta, sì, forse. Voglio assolutamente trovare quell'uomo! Perché? Non lo so neppure io, ma è la cosa più importante per me adesso.

"Naturalmente mio cugino ha bisogno di una foto o di un disegno dell'uomo" dice Max.

"Una foto? Un disegno? Ma io non ho nessuna foto né disegno."

"Questo è un problema. Alfredo non può cercare una persona con una descrizione così come l'hai data tu… Un barbone, statura media, capelli grigi, barba grigia. Tutti i barboni sono così…"

"Aspetta! Ho un'idea. Possiamo chiedere a qualcuno che disegna bene di fare l'identikit di quell'uomo."

"Sì, ma chi?"

"Io conosco una persona che disegna da artista."

"Ma certo… la conosco anch'io!"

Questa persona è Sibilla. Tutti in classe sanno che Sibilla fa dei disegni molto belli, ritratti di donne, di uomini e di ragazzi. Sembrano veri!

È l'una e venti. La lezione è finita finalmente. Andiamo da lei e le spieghiamo in poche parole la faccenda.

"Certo che voglio aiutarti" dice lei "però c'è un problema."

"Quale?" chiedo io.

"Io di pomeriggio non posso uscire. Cioè, devo sempre dire alla mamma dove vado."

"Bene, puoi dire che vieni a casa mia."

"No, mia mamma non vuole. Non posso andare da sola a casa dei ragazzi. Però… però forse ho la soluzione. Oggi ho lezione di aerobica. Esco per andare a lezione e invece vengo da te, cosa dici?"

"Grazie, sei molto gentile." Che frase originale! L'unica che mi è venuta in mente.

Sibilla arriva a casa mia alle quattro in punto.

Betta ha preparato, per me e la mia amica, la sua specialità: crostata[15] di fragole. È la prima volta che una ragazza viene a casa mia!

Vado io ad aprire la porta. Sibilla è vestita con i jeans e un maglioncino rosso. È bellissima!

"Entra…" dico io, e sento un grande caldo. Forse sono diventato rosso in faccia?

Lei mi sorride poi guarda la grande sala e la scala che porta al piano superiore.

"Che bella casa hai!" dice. "È vero che c'è anche la piscina?"

"Sì, è nel giardino, ma adesso è vuota. La riempiamo soltanto in estate."

Saliamo per le scale fino alla mia camera.

"Accidenti, ma quanto è grande la tua camera!" dice.

Grande? A me non sembra. Mi sembra una camera come le altre. Con il letto, un armadio, la scrivania, il computer… Alle pareti sono appesi dei poster di film di fantascienza.

"Anche a te piacciono i film di fantascienza, vedo. Io ho un poster di *Blade Runner*."

---

[15] *crostata*: dolce italiano fatto con pasta frolla e marmellata.

"*Blade Runner*… Oh, sì… il film con Harrison Ford. Anche a te quindi piace la fantascienza. Strano! In genere alle ragazze piacciono soltanto i film d'amore o cose del genere."

Lei sembra irritata.

"Ecco… le solite cattiverie sulle ragazze. I maschi dicono che ci piacciono soltanto le cose d'amore, ma non è vero! A me piace la fantascienza e anche i film western, se lo vuoi sapere."

Io non so cosa dire. So solo che mi piace sempre di più.

"Ho voglia di baciarla" penso "come fanno nei film."

Ma naturalmente non faccio niente. Invece le offro una fetta di torta.

"L'ha fatta Betta" dico.

"Chi è Betta?"

"È una ragazza, cioè una donna. Ormai ha ventiquattro anni. Da più di dieci anni abita qui con noi. Sai, Betta non ha famiglia. I suoi genitori sono morti quando era bambina."

"Mi dispiace, poverina…" Dalla borsa della palestra prende un album da disegno. "Adesso però mettiamoci al lavoro! Alle sei devo essere assolutamente a casa." Si siede davanti a me. La matita in mano, concentrata, mi sembra una vera professionista.

"Allora cominciamo. Com'è la forma del viso?"

"Ovale, sì lunga e ovale."

Lei disegna e poi mi domanda la stessa cosa per gli occhi, il naso, la bocca, le guance, il collo, i capelli. Disegna per quasi un'ora.

Adesso mi mostra il disegno.

"Allora?" chiede.

"Sì" rispondo "perfetto! Sei veramente brava."

"Grazie. Ma adesso devo assolutamente andare. Cinque minuti di ritardo e mia mamma entra nel panico."

Prima di uscire, mi viene vicino e mi dà un bacio sulla guancia.

Sono innamorato.

7
Il cugino di Max

Alle otto suona il campanello di casa mia. So chi è. È il cugino di Max. Viene a prendere il disegno. Mi è arrivato un sms di Max per avvertirmi.

Vado io alla porta.

I miei genitori non devono assolutamente vedere il cugino di Max. Fortunatamente ha una grande fretta. La sigaretta in bocca, le mani nelle tasche del giubbotto nero, prende il disegno e chiede soltanto:

"I bigliettoni[16]?"

"Ecco" rispondo io e gli do una busta con i trecento euro.

"Ti faccio sapere" fa lui e riparte con la sua moto.

Finita la cena, torno in camera a guardare un po' di televisione.

Dopo dieci minuti arriva Betta.

"Riccardo, io l'ho visto. Quel ragazzo deve avere almeno vent'anni… non è un tuo compagno di classe!"

"Non dire niente a mamma e a papà, per favore!" faccio io.

"Certo che no. Ma mi dici che cosa stai combinando[17]?"

"Uno di questi giorni ti racconto tutto" rispondo io.

So che mi posso fidare di Betta.

"Va bene, come vuoi" dice lei.

Il fine settimana è noioso. Alcuni parenti vengono in visita a casa nostra e poi io devo studiare italiano e matematica. Passo la sera del sabato al telefono con Sibilla, anche lei a casa, e ci raccontiamo tante cose. Max invece è uscito con Elisa, la sua nuova ragazza.

Finalmente è lunedì. Prima della lezione, Max mi dà un foglio in una busta chiusa. Sopra c'è scritto: da parte di Freddy. Apro la busta sotto il banco. Leggo:

Ho trovato il tuo barbone. Sta sempre vicino al museo della scienza e della tecnica. Va a mangiare alla chiesa dei Francescani[18] che è lì vicino. Lo puoi trovare lì quasi sempre di sera. Non so come si chiama, ma deve essere un ex professore o qualcosa del genere. Infatti lo chiamano «il professore».

"Allora?" mi chiede Max durante l'intervallo.

"Ho delle indicazioni piuttosto precise" dico io "adesso voglio andare a parlare con lui."

"Come fai? I tuoi genitori ti accompagnano dappertutto!"

In quel momento arriva Sibilla.

"Allora?" chiede anche lei.

---

[16] *bigliettoni:* (in gergo) i soldi, le banconote.

[17] *cosa stai combinando?:* cosa stai facendo?

[18] *Francescani:* frati dell'ordine di San Francesco.

Io le mostro il biglietto di Freddy.

"Ci sono informazioni molto utili. Adesso so dove trovarlo. Il problema sono i miei genitori. Non posso uscire di sera."

"Puoi dire che vai a casa di Max a studiare e che resti lì a mangiare."

"Mio padre mi accompagna di sicuro."

"Non c'è problema. Ti fai accompagnare. Poi da casa di Max vai dove devi andare. Dopo torni a casa di Max. Lì ti può venire a prendere tuo padre."

"È una buona idea" dico io.

"Hai paura?" chiede Max.

"No, che cavolo dici?" faccio io offeso. Non deve dire queste cose davanti a Sibilla! " Non sono un bambino."

"Per quando allora?" domanda ancora Max.

"Domani pomeriggio. Non voglio perdere tempo."

"Posso venire con te?" chiede Sibilla all'uscita da scuola.

"No, grazie Sibilla" rispondo io "questa è una cosa che devo sbrigare[19] da solo."

---

[19] *sbrigare:* fare, risolvere.

PARTE 3

8
Beniamino

Va tutto come deve andare. Sulla mappa della città cerco la chiesa dei frati Francescani. Ci arrivo che sono quasi le sette. Ai miei genitori ho detto che sono andato a mangiare da Max.

Sono davanti alla chiesa. Entro. La porta è aperta: mi trovo nella sala della mensa. È una grande stanza con tavoli di legno. A ogni tavolo stanno seduti uomini e donne. Devono essere una ventina.

"Non può essere tanto difficile trovare il *mio* uomo" penso. Faccio qualche passo verso il primo tavolo quando un frate mi chiede:

"Di che cosa hai bisogno, ragazzo?"

Intanto mi scruta. Forse pensa:

"Che cosa ci fa uno così in un posto come questo?"

"Cerco una persona, signore" rispondo io.

"Non chiamarmi signore, io sono fratello Matteo."

"Sì, fratello Matteo."

"Chi cerchi? "chiede ancora il frate.

"Una persona, un… parente…"

"Un parente?"

"Sì, mio zio, mi hanno detto che mio zio è qui."

"Tuo zio" ripete quello. "Va bene. Da' un'occhiata[20] allora!"

"Grazie sign… fratello Matteo."

Mi avvicino ad un tavolo, quando vedo un uomo che si alza. Cammina velocemente verso la porta. È di media statura, porta un giaccone scuro e una sciarpa. Riconosco i capelli grigi lunghi sulle spalle.

"È lui" penso "è lui e mi scappa di nuovo."

Sotto lo sguardo stupito di fratello Matteo, esco di corsa dalla sala. Arrivo in strada. Vuota. Guardo di qua, guardo di là, non c'è proprio nessuno!

"Che fine ha fatto, accidenti[21]?"

Improvvisamente mi sento afferrare un braccio.

Grido. Penso agli uomini con le maschere. Ma non sono loro. Invece

---

[20] *dà un'occhiata:* guarda.

[21] *accidenti:* esclamazione che indica stupore, qualche volta spavento.

è l'uomo dai capelli grigi!

Sono contento: l'ho trovato finalmente. Ma lui non sembra contento. Mi fa una domanda dietro l'altra: "Chi sei? Che cosa vuoi da me? Perché mi hai fatto cercare?"

"Perché lei è l'uomo che mi ha salvato."

"Che cosa racconti? Salvato? Che cos'è questa storia?"

"Sì, lei è la persona che io ho visto dalla finestrella della cantina. Io sono il ragazzo rapito."

"Ma lasciami stare, per favore!" dice lui e sembra veramente arrabbiato. "Tu sei matto!"

Vuole convincermi che non è lui, ma io so che è lui. Perciò dico gentile, ma deciso:

"Io sono sicurissimo, signore, che quell'uomo è lei."

"E come fai ad esserne così sicuro?" chiede.

"Era notte, ma io l'ho vista bene. Non posso dimenticare la sua faccia. Per me era come un angelo, un angelo salvatore…"

Lui ride.

"Oh buon Dio…un angelo salvatore… "

"Sì, signore" ripeto io.

"Beh, devo dire che sei un gran testardo."

"Grazie signore."

L'uomo ride di nuovo.

"Grazie di che? Non è un complimento."

"Non è più così freddo…" penso. "Questo è il momento buono."

"Vuole venire a mangiare qualcosa con me?" gli chiedo.

"Volentieri. Quando si ha fame, è difficile dire no a un invito a cena.."

Porto l'uomo in un ristorante che conosco. Sono andato lì a mangiare con i miei compagni di classe l'anno scorso. Non si spende tanto. I miei quaranta euro bastano senz'altro.

Ci sediamo a un tavolo in un angolo. Viene un cameriere. Ha la faccia seria, sembra seccato. Ordiniamo due pizze quattro stagioni.

"Non gli devo essere simpatico" dice il mio amico vagabondo.

"È che forse insieme siamo strani" commento io.

"Già, tu con il maglioncino di cashmere, le scarpe da trecento euro, l'orologio di marca e la faccia da «figlio di papà», io sporco e malvestito proprio come un… barbone." Ride forte.

Non rispondo. Adesso sono io un po' seccato: mi dà fastidio sentire parlare ancora una volta del mio denaro. Devo dire che però sui vestiti ha ragione: sono proprio i vestiti di un ragazzo ricco!

"Da domani cambio look, accidenti!" mi dico.

In quel momento arrivano le due pizze più una coca cola e un grosso bicchiere di birra. L'uomo beve tutta la birra, poi mangiamo la pizza.

Io sono ancora a metà e lui l'ha già mangiata tutta.

Ordino un'altra birra per l'uomo e poi chiedo:

"Beve molta birra, signore?"

"Se mi stai chiedendo se sono un alcolizzato, la risposta è no. Non ancora almeno."

Si alza in piedi.

"Adesso devo andare. Alle nove mi chiude il dormitorio[22]. Se non sono lì entro mezz'ora dovrò dormire all'addiaccio[23]."

"All'addiaccio?" penso io stupito. "Che parola difficile in bocca ad un vagabondo!"

Ma non dico niente. Invece voglio chiedergli altre cose.

Usciamo dalla pizzeria.

"Senta, signore…" comincio.

"Non chiamarmi signore. Io sono Beniamino. E dammi del tu!"

"Sì, Beniamino. Io ti ho cercato…"

"Mi hai fatto cercare…"

"Sì, ti ho fatto cercare perché vorrei ringraziarti. Io ti… ti devo la vita."

"Lo so."

"Non ti ho neppure ringraziato. Sei andato via. Ma perché?"

"Perché avevo paura, paura della polizia, paura dei criminali. Se sanno che ho chiamato la polizia, sono morto."

"Quindi anche tu hai paura?" chiedo io.

"Sì, certo."

"Ma perché non sei andato alla polizia? Loro possono…"

"Proteggermi? No, nessuno protegge uno come me. Io sono un vagabondo, non ho casa, non ho lavoro. A nessuno interessa se vivo o no."

Un momento di silenzio e poi gli faccio una domanda. Per me la risposta è molto importante:

"Sai chi sono i miei rapitori?"

---

[22] *dormitorio:* dove dormono le persone che non hanno casa o soldi sufficienti per un albergo.

[23] *all'addiaccio:* all'aperto.

"Li ho visti in faccia. Era notte, ma li ho visti. Però non so i loro nomi e non so dove abitano."

"Erano in due, vero?"

"Tre. C'era anche una terza persona. Credo una donna, ma non sono sicuro."

Io ho ancora un domanda.

"Cosa credi? Mi... vogliono rapire ancora?"

La voce mi trema.

"Non devi avere paura" mi dice Beniamino. Mette la sua grande mano sulla mia. "In genere non ritentano un rapimento sulla stessa persona. Ecco il dormitorio. È tardi. Sono quasi le nove. Chiama un taxi per tornare a casa."

Sì, è meglio prendere un taxi. Lo chiamo con il cellulare. Ho ancora quindici euro: mi bastano per pagare il viaggio fino a casa di Max! Beniamino aspetta con me.

"Posso rivederti?" domando.

"Non è prudente."

"Ma così di sera... non ci vede nessuno..."

"Che cosa vuoi ancora da me? Mi hai parlato, mi hai ringraziato, abbiamo mangiato insieme. Adesso cosa vuoi?"

"Io voglio...voglio diventare tuo amico."

Il taxi è qui. Gli stringo la mano e dico:

"La prossima settimana vengo come oggi alla mensa."

Beniamino non dice niente. Io sono già sul taxi.

Ci salutiamo con un sorriso.

9
Problemi

La mattina dopo mi sveglio prima del solito. Alle sette e un quarto sono già in cucina a fare colazione.

"Come mai a quest'ora?" chiede mia mamma. "C'è qualcosa che non va?"

"No, anzi..." Le rispondo con un gran sorriso. Mi sento allegro e felice. Mangio con appetito la brioche al cioccolato e bevo il latte con il caffè. Intanto è arrivata Betta. Anche lei mangia la brioche e beve il suo caffè. Ci alziamo da tavola nello stesso momento. Faccio qualche passo verso la porta.

Mi volto per salutarle. Vedo che mamma e Betta mi scrutano.

"Cosa succede?" chiedo anche se so perché sono così sorprese.

"Ma come ti sei vestito?" domanda Betta.

"Perché?"

"Sembri un no global."

"Sembri un .... barbone" dice la mamma.

"Uffaaa… Non ho più voglia di vestirmi da bravo signorino."

E con ciò esco dalla cucina. Sento la voce della mamma che mi grida dietro: "Con quei jeans vecchi e lisi[24] prendi freddo".

"Ma che freddo e freddo" penso io "sto benissimo così."

Dopo mezz'ora la nuova prova: mio padre che mi accompagna a scuola. Ma lui parla tutto il tempo al cellulare e non nota niente. Solo quando siamo davanti a scuola e mi saluta, fa un commento sulla mia maglietta:

"Che strana! È così vecchia che sembra sporca."

"Non è sporca, papà" rispondo io. Ed entro a scuola.

Anche in classe tutti notano che sono vestito in modo diverso, ma nessuno dice niente. Il mio amico Max invece dice:

"Ehi, Ricky, come sei vestito? Vuoi essere come il tuo amico barbone?"

"Non chiamarlo barbone!" rispondo.

"Stai bene vestito così" commenta invece Sibilla.

"Dici questo perché sei innamorata cotta e stracotta[25]" dice Max. "Può venire anche vestito da uomo delle nevi, e tu «oh Ricky, quanto sei bello!»" .

"Vai al diavolo!" fa Sibilla e diventa tutta rossa.

Questo prima dell'inizio delle lezioni. All'intervallo voglio parlare ancora con Sibilla, ma lei sta con un'amica. Forse perché è offesa o imbarazzata per le parole di Max… *Innamorata cotta e stracotta.*

Io racconto a Max cosa è successo. Il giorno prima, infatti, non ho avuto tempo. Sono arrivato a casa sua molto tardi.

"Una bella storia" dice il mio amico. "Sono sicuro che puoi convincerlo a identificare i tuoi rapitori."

All'uscita di scuola di nuovo mi avvicino a Sibilla.

"Mio padre è qui in macchina. Possiamo accompagnarti a casa" dico.

---

[24] *lisi*: consumati, rovinati.

[25] *innamorata cotta e stracotta*: espressione giovanile per dire "molto innamorata".

"No, grazie" mi risponde lei secca.

Io non sono arrabbiato con lei. In fondo la capisco. Vorrei dirle mille cose: che mi piace tanto, che penso a lei giorno e notte, che anch'io sono innamorato di lei, cotto e stracotto, come dice Max.

Invece non dico niente e rimango lì in strada come uno sciocco a guardarla allontanarsi con le sue gambe lunghe e i capelli neri neri sotto la luce del sole.

Un brutto lunedì e una brutta settimana. L'incubo ogni notte, Sibilla arrabbiata, Max sui libri perché prende tanti brutti voti.

Domenica sono invitato a una festa a casa di un compagno di classe. Abita proprio vicino alla chiesa dei Francescani. In realtà quando decido di andare alla festa, non penso a questo. Spero invece di vedere Sibilla.

Quando arrivo alla festa, rimango deluso: ci sono quasi tutti i miei compagni di classe, ma proprio lei manca.

"È malata" dice una sua amica "o almeno così ha detto sua mamma."

"Perché? Non ci credi?"

"Oh, tu non sai com'è la mamma di Sibilla. Pensa ancora di vivere nell'Ottocento. Non vuole che Sibilla vada a queste feste."

Da quel momento la festa non m'interessa più. Gli altri ballano, io sto alla finestra. Da qui posso vedere la chiesa.

"Sono le sei e mezza" penso. "A quest'ora ho visto Beniamino l'altra volta. Adesso scendo e magari lo incontro."

Lo dico a Max. Sta ballando stretto stretto con una ragazza. Mi dice sì sì, e io vado.

Esco, vado alla chiesa. Entro nella mensa, ma la trovo vuota. C'è soltanto un uomo che pulisce per terra.

"La domenica si mangia più tardi" mi dice.

"Va bene – penso – in questi giorni sono proprio sfortunato. Allora devo tornare alla festa."

Cammino per la piazza, quando lo vedo. È seduto su una panchina e legge.

"Ah, come sono felice – mi dico e di nuovo mi domando – perché sono così contento di vederlo?"

Vado verso la panchina e mi siedo accanto a lui.

Lo saluto con un ciao e lui mi risponde, ma non mi guarda in faccia.

"Che cosa leggi?" chiedo.

Mi mostra il libro e io leggo il titolo ad alta voce: "I sonetti di Shakespeare…"

"Ti piacciono?"

"Non li ho mai letti…"

"Ah ah…" l'uomo richiude il libro. "Ti piace la poesia?"

"La poesia no, però mi piace leggere."

"Cosa?"

"Libri, romanzi. Soprattutto gialli e fantascienza."

"Tipici generi di lettura per adolescenti. Generi di consumo[26], ma non solo…"

"Parli come un professore."

"Però non lo sono" dice lui e si alza in piedi." Sono un barbone. Come vedi."

Anch'io mi alzo.

"Come mai qui? Il nostro appuntamento non era per mercoledì?"

"Sono qui per una festa…" Indico con il dito l'appartamento dove c'è la festa.

"Ma non ti piace."

"No, cioè non è così male. Soltanto che volevo vederti, parlare con te."

"Non capisco. Che cosa vuoi da me? Comunque devo andare, la mensa sta aprendo e io ho una fame terribile."

"Hai voglia di mangiare qualcosa con me?"

"Non devi tornare alla festa?"

"No, posso fare quello che voglio."

Non è vero, però è vero che ho tempo perché i miei genitori mi credono alla festa. Ho ancora almeno due ore.

Beniamino sembra indeciso e io:

"Eh dai! Andiamo di nuovo al «Mangia Mangia»!"

"D'accordo. Come ho già detto, non si può rifiutare un pasto caldo."

10
Un nuovo amico

Al ristorante Beniamino mi chiede a che ora devo essere a casa.

"Mio padre viene a prendermi alle nove alla festa" rispondo.

---

[26] *di consumo:* letteratura di genere "basso", di scarso valore letterario.

"Sono preoccupati, vero?"

"Chi?"

"I tuoi genitori."

"Mia mamma sì."

"E il papà?"

"Non lo so. Lui sta poco a casa. Lavora tutto il tempo. La sua famiglia è l'azienda."

"Questo vuol dire che parli poco con lui?"

"Praticamente per niente. Ogni tanto mi chiede come va la scuola e cose così. Però se ho un problema, non vado a raccontarlo a lui. Non gli interessa niente, del resto."

"Io penso di sì."

"Perché lo dici? Non conosci mio padre."

"No, però so come vanno queste cose. I padri lavorano non tanto per se stessi, ma per la moglie e i figli, per la famiglia, insomma. Devi pensare che tu vivi bene perché tuo padre lavora così tanto."

La pizza intanto arriva: anche questa volta non ho una gran fame.

Beniamino invece mangia velocemente.

"Tu hai dei figli?" chiedo.

"No" risponde lui secco "ma ti ripeto: so come vanno queste cose. Non sono sempre stato un barbone."

"Da quanto… voglio dire…" sono imbarazzato a fargli questa domanda.

Ma lui mi legge nel pensiero e mi chiede:

"Vuoi sapere da quanto faccio questa vita?"

"Sì."

"Da qualche anno, quattro, cinque credo…"

"Non ne sei sicuro?"

"No, per noi barboni il tempo non è importante. È una delle belle cose del nostro mestiere."

"Mestiere?"

"Beh, si fa per dire. Però, anche se non lavoro, ho delle attività anch'io."

"Cioè?"

"Mi devo procurare del cibo, e questo mi prende molto tempo. Poi devo cercarmi un letto per ogni notte, anche questo non è sempre facile. Inoltre devo pensare a difendermi, perché ragazzo mio, *homo homini*

28

lupus[27]. Mi rimane comunque molto tempo per leggere e qualche volta vado anche al cinema."

"Conosco questa frase in latino. Significa l'uomo è lupo per l'uomo" dico io.

"Bravo!"

"Tu eri un prof, ne sono sicuro. Anche come hai detto bravo adesso, proprio come un prof."

Lui ride, ma non risponde. Ha finito la pizza.

"È ora di andare, vero?" chiede Beniamino.

Sì, è ora. Anche se non ho voglia.

"Alla festa ci sono i tuoi amici?"

"C'è Max."

"Chi è Max?"

"Il mio unico amico."

"Lo conosci da tanto?"

"Tantissimo… da tutta la vita praticamente."

Beniamino ride. Quando ride mostra denti bianchi e giovani.

"Quanti anni può avere?" mi chiedo. "Quaranta, cinquanta?" Ma non dico niente. Invece gli domando:

"Tu hai amici?"

"Amici?" risponde Beniamino. "Ne avevo un tempo. Poi in un giorno li ho persi tutti. Dal primo all'ultimo."

"Allora non erano veri amici."

"Forse" dice lui. Ha una faccia triste adesso.

"Scusa, forse ti ho ricordato qualcosa di brutto?"

"No, sciocchezze, solo sciocchezze. Non m'importa più adesso."

Prima di tornare alla festa, gli chiedo se ci vediamo mercoledì.

"Va bene…" risponde Beniamino. "Anche se può essere pericoloso."

"Tu credi?"

"Non lo so. Forse no. Probabilmente adesso i tuoi rapitori sono molto lontano da qui."

Sono le nove meno dieci, appena in tempo. Salgo e prendo la giacca.

Max è ancora con la ragazza. Mi saluta. Suona il cellulare: è papà. Scendo e torno a casa.

---

[27] *homo homini lupus:* frase latina che significa letteralmente "l'uomo è lupo per l'uomo", cioè l'uomo è egoista e malvagio verso gli altri uomini, è nemico dei suoi simili.

Per tre giorni Sibilla non viene a scuola. Allora vuol dire che è veramente ammalata, ma io non posso telefonarle. La sua amica mi ha detto: "Non devi chiamarla! Sua mamma non vuole."

Max invece è sempre insieme a Elisa. È una "bellona", alta alta e sembra una modella ed è sempre vestita sexy, ma a me non piace. La trovo così sciocca e vuota... Parla solo di cose "alla moda", di "bella gente" e di moto.

"Sei innamorato?" domando a Max in classe.

"Innamorato è una parola grossa. Mi piace e basta" risponde lui. E poi chiede:

"Questa sera vedi il tuo barbone?"

"Non chiamarlo barbone" rispondo io irritato "e comunque sì."

"Quindi ti fai accompagnare da me prima?"

"Sì, ti dispiace?"

"No, va bene."

Alla sei e trenta mi incontro con Beniamino alla panchina della piazza.

"Oggi andiamo in un posto che conosco e offro io" dice.

"Ma tu non puoi!"

"Certo che posso. Anch'io qualche volta ho soldi. Dopo tutto compro i libri e vado al cinema. E poi, non ti preoccupare! Ti porto in un posto molto economico[28]. Ci andiamo a piedi. Sono quindici minuti."

"Va bene."

"Cosa hai detto ai tuoi?" chiede Beniamino.

"La solita cosa... che sono da Max."

"Il tuo miglior amico."

"Esattamente."

"E non hai la fidanzata?"

"Fidanzata?" rido. "Non si dice fidanzata."

"Ah, OK. Come dite? Compagna, donna, ragazza?"

"Ragazza. No, non ho una ragazza, ma c'è Sibilla."

"Sibilla, Sibilla... che bel nome antico."

Parlo con lui di Sibilla. E ascolto per la prima volta consigli, veri e saggi consigli.

Siamo al ristorante, una sala con i tavoli di legno dove mangiamo

---

[28] *economico:* non caro, che costa poco.

pasta e fagioli.

"Vedi" dice Beniamino "in amore bisogna essere attenti."

"Cioè?"

"Max ha detto che si capisce che Sibilla è innamorata di te. Lei adesso si sente scoperta, vulnerabile[29]. Tu, e gli altri, conoscete adesso i suoi sentimenti. I sentimenti sono forse ciò che di più segreto e di più prezioso ognuno di noi possiede. Adesso tu devi…"

"Cosa?"

"Semplicemente farle capire *i tuoi* sentimenti."

"Per me è difficile" dico io. "Soprattutto «dopo»."

"Dopo cosa? Dopo il rapimento?"

"Sì, sono ancora più chiuso. Non riesco a parlare con nessuno di quello che sento."

"Vuoi parlarne con me?"

"Sì." E parlo, parlo a lungo come non ho mai parlato con nessuno.

Adesso capisco perché cerco Beniamino. Perché mi capisce.

11
Ancora paura

Sono quasi le nove quando usciamo dal ristorante. Dobbiamo tornare alla piazza. Non c'è nessuno per le strade: è sera, è buio, fa freddo.

Stiamo camminando su una strada stretta quando improvvisamente arriva una macchina. A tutta velocità. Verso di noi.

Beniamino grida:

"Corri! Riccardo, corri!"

Saliamo sul marciapiede e la macchina ci segue. Io ho paura.

Corro e corro. Mi sento prendere per una mano, e trascinare[30] con tutto il corpo in un cortile attraverso il portone aperto.

Mi ritrovo per terra. Alcune finestre del palazzo sul cortile si aprono.

Beniamino è in piedi, mi dà la mano per rialzarmi. Aspettiamo qualche minuto. Poi usciamo.

Io non riesco a parlare. Ho ancora tanta paura.

Beniamino mi consiglia di chiamare un taxi col cellulare.

"Io mi faccio portare in qualche posto in cui non mi trovano e tu

---

[29] *vulnerabile:* che è facile ferire perché senza difesa.

[30] *trascinare:* portare.

direttamente a casa" dice.

Sì, meglio non a casa di Max. Se penso solo che devo salire le scale da solo, mi sento male dalla paura. Perché adesso è chiaro: i rapitori non sono molto lontano, come ha detto Beniamino.

Saliamo su un taxi.

"Non ci possiamo più vedere adesso, vero?" chiedo. "Alla fine è successo... avevi ragione."

"Su che cosa?"

"Sul pericolo. È tutta colpa mia."

"No, è anche colpa mia. Sono stato uno sciocco. Ma va bene, è inutile adesso e... Che cosa c'è? Sei bianco come un lenzuolo. Hai ancora paura?"

Beniamino mi circonda la spalla con il braccio.

"No, adesso molto meno" dico io.

"Può tornare."

"Cosa?"

"La paura."

"Negli incubi?"

"Forse e non solo. Dobbiamo fare qualcosa. Contro i rapitori, voglio dire. Non puoi vivere tutta la vita così, nella paura. Non è giusto."

"Cosa possiamo fare adesso?"

"Qualcosa da fare c'è" risponde Beniamino. "Ma adesso è troppo tardi per parlarne. Io sono arrivato."

Il taxi passa in quel momento in una grande piazza e Beniamino chiede al tassista di fermarsi lì. Prima di scendere mi dice:

"Ti chiamo sul cellulare domani, così parliamo."

Io voglio abbracciarlo, ma non lo faccio. Ancora una volta non riesco a fare quello che desidero. I sentimenti stanno dentro di me in un blocco di ghiaccio. "Forse sono fatto così" penso.

Arrivo a casa alle nove.

"Mi ha accompagnato la mamma di Max" dico ai miei.

Mi rispondono "bene, bene". Non hanno notato niente. Per fortuna.

La mattina seguente, subito dopo la fine delle lezioni, mi telefona Beniamino.

"Ciao. Devo essere veloce perché ho pochi soldi. Sei solo?"

"Sì."

"Ho pensato questo, Riccardo: devo fare un identikit dei rapitori."

"Ma tu…"

"Lasciami finire. Non voglio andare alla polizia. Non posso. Però posso fare un identikit. Tu devi conoscere un bravo disegnatore. Ricordo bene quel ragazzo, Freddy, mi pare… Aveva un disegno, il mio ritratto. Chi lo ha fatto?"

"Sibilla."

"Ah, la famosa Sibilla… Ora ascoltami bene! Devo incontrare questa Sibilla e deve fare gli identikit dei due rapitori. Ma senza di te."

"Perché senza di me?"

"Perché i rapitori seguono te, non me. Giusto?"

"Sì, hai ragione."

"Allora fa' così. Chiedi al tuo amico Max di accompagnare Sibilla all'appuntamento con me."

"OK. L'appuntamento dove?"

"Dopodomani, ore 18: Piazza delle Armi. Li trovo io. "

"Sibilla fa i disegni e poi? Cosa vuoi fare con questi disegni?"

"Delle fotocopie e le do a certi miei amici."

"Barbo… cioè vagabondi come te?"

"Esattamente, facciamo i barboni detective, cosa ne dici?"

Il giorno dopo a scuola per fortuna c'è Sibilla.

Non sembra più arrabbiata con me. Mi parla e mi sorride.

"Come va?" mi chiede nell'intervallo. E io le racconto tutto.

Infine le domando:

"Puoi andare con Max all'appuntamento?"

"Sì, certo, però devo raccontare qualche bugia alla mamma. Posso dire che vado da un'amica a studiare."

Il giorno dopo fila tutto liscio[31].

Beniamino adesso ha il suo identikit e può cominciare la *sua* indagine.

---

[31] *fila tutto liscio:* va tutto bene.

PARTE 4

12
Il sacchetto

Passano tre giorni. Il terzo giorno mi chiama Beniamino. Ha di nuovo pochi soldi e può stare al telefono solo qualche minuto.

"Sono sicuro che li troviamo" dice.

"Quando ci vediamo?" chiedo io.

"Appena possibile" risponde lui.

Ho una gran voglia di vedere Beniamino. Con lui riesco veramente a parlare. Per fortuna adesso ho un'altra amica: Sibilla. A scuola passiamo insieme ogni intervallo (tanto Max sta sempre con la bellona), ogni momento libero è per lei, ogni sera il telefono di casa scotta[32] dopo le nostre lunghissime telefonate.

"Sei cotto, cotto e stracotto" dice Max. "Almeno esci qualche volta con lei. O vuoi parlare e basta?"

Max non capisce. Per lui le ragazze devono essere solo belle e «disponibili»! Niente di più.

E comunque il suo consiglio è assolutamente inutile perché io *voglio* uscire con Sibilla! Ma è difficile. Infatti lei ha poca libertà a causa di sua mamma e io a causa della mia brutta avventura. Non sono libero e non mi sento libero. Ancora meno da quella sera con Beniamino, quando la macchina ha tentato di investirmi. Cosa che non ho detto ai miei genitori.

Ho ancora paura. Ma questo posso dirlo a una persona sola: Beniamino. E lui, da quel famoso giorno si tiene lontano da me. Mi ha solo chiamato diverse volte per dirmi: "Non riusciamo a sapere niente. Nessuno conosce gli uomini del disegno... Forse non sono di questa città, o almeno non sono criminali di questa città..." Perché i criminali, così dice Beniamino, tra di loro si conoscono!

Ogni volta che chiama, io gli chiedo quando ci possiamo vedere.

"Mi sembri un'innamorata..." dice lui. "Perbacco, pensa alla tua bella Sibilla!"

Io non rispondo niente, ma so che Beniamino capisce. E allora con la sua bella voce tranquilla conclude:

"Tempo al tempo, tempo al tempo. Devi avere pazienza, ragazzo mio."

---

[32] *scotta:* è caldissimo.

Passa così un mese. Finché viene febbraio.

"Domenica i miei genitori vanno in campagna" dice Sibilla. "E io ho detto che vado a studiare da un'amica."

"Ah bene. Vai da Letizia?" chiedo io.

"No, veramente…" E mi guarda.

"Mi sta chiedendo se voglio uscire con lei? – penso – Usciamo insieme? Non ci posso credere. Finalmente!"

"Sei sicuro di non aver problemi?"

"Assolutamente no."

Invece sono preoccupato. Se esco con Sibilla, devo stare solo in città. Forse non ci riesco. Forse ho troppa paura.

Ma il giorno dell'appuntamento, dopo una notte di incubi, decido: paura o non paura, voglio uscire.

Come sempre, racconto ai miei genitori che vado da Max. È Betta che mi accompagna questa volta. Mio padre non può e mia mamma non guida.

Siamo in macchina io e Betta. Sembra nervosa. Forse perché alle quattro di solito ha la lezione di danza e oggi non è andata. Per accompagnare me.

"Mi prendi le sigarette?" mi chiede e indica il cassetto vicino al posto di guida. Nel cassetto ci sono tante cose e io devo cercare il pacchetto di sigarette che è in fondo. Quando lo tiro fuori cadono sul pavimento delle carte. Betta si accende la sigaretta, io raccolgo le carte da terra. Uno è un foglio e l'altro il sacchetto di un panettiere. Sul sacchetto c'è scritto: Stelladi. Sento il cuore che batte forte.

Betta non si accorge di niente. Continua a fumare, gli occhi sulla strada piena di macchine. Io rimetto il foglio e il sacchetto nel cassetto. Giusto in tempo. Betta ferma la macchina.

"Siamo arrivati" dice.

Scendo dalla macchina e salgo da Max. Il portone del suo palazzo è sempre aperto. Arrivo al suo appartamento e suono, ma non risponde nessuno.

Accidenti, Max è fuori. E adesso?

Scendo in strada e cammino veloce verso il parco delle Rose. Lì ho l'appuntamento con Sibilla. Sono nervoso e agitato. Ma non più per la paura. Per il sospetto. Un terribile sospetto: Betta è implicata[33] nel mio rapimento!

---

[33] *è implicata*: ha qualcosa a che fare con…

Aspetto Sibilla su una panchina del parco.

Prendo il diario che porto sempre con me e comincio a scrivere. È un consiglio di Beniamino: *quando non hai le idee chiare, scrivi…*

E io scrivo. Solo per cinque minuti perché arriva Sibilla. Bella e sorridente, mi chiede:

"Che cosa stai scrivendo?"

"Niente" rispondo io e metto via il quaderno.

"Come stai?" domanda gentile.

"Bene e tu?"

"Benissimo. Dai! andiamo."

Prima deve andare un po' per negozi a cercare un regalo per sua mamma. Io per tutto il tempo non dico una parola. Lei invece parla e ride.

Dice anche:

"Sono felice che sei qui con me."

Finalmente trova il regalo per la madre: una borsa.

Quando siamo fuori dal negozio, mi dice spazientita:

"Senti, forse è meglio che ce ne andiamo a casa adesso. Vedo che non sei di buon umore[34]."

Io apro la bocca, ma la richiudo subito. Come sempre mi mancano le parole. Lei si arrabbia.

"Ho capito, ciao." Fa qualche passo.

"Sei uno sciocco! Un cretino! Un idiota" mi dico e arrivo alle sue spalle.

"Ascolta Sibilla" dico "mi dispiace. È che è successo qualcosa…"

Siamo seduti in un bar del centro commerciale, davanti a due tazze di cioccolata calda. Io racconto a Sibilla del sacchetto.

"Hai deciso che cosa fare?" chiede lei.

"No."

"Vuoi andare alla polizia?"

"Noooo… Scherzi? È solo un sospetto."

"Però non puoi continuare a vivere con lei con questo sospetto, no?"

"Sì, ma non so cosa fare."

"Io ho un'idea. Entra nella sua camera, guarda in giro, vedi se trovi qualcosa."

"Ci ho pensato anch'io. Ma mi sembra una cosa tanto orribile da

---

[34] *non sei di buon umore:* non sei allegro.

fare… Io voglio molto bene a Betta."

Però poi cambio idea e dico: "Sì, hai ragione. Faccio come dici."

È sera. Voglio accompagnare Sibilla a casa.

"No, assolutamente no" dice lei " dopo quello che mi hai raccontato, non voglio. È rischioso per te, troppo rischioso."

"È stato rischioso anche uscire oggi, e anche essere qui in mezzo alla strada alle sei di sera è rischioso" rispondo io. "Sibilla, ascolta, Beniamino ha detto bene: non posso più vivere nella paura. Quindi… ti accompagno."

E faccio così.

A un semaforo mi dà la mano come un bambino alla mamma. Io la stringo nella mia. E mi sento felice. Nonostante il sospetto, nonostante Betta, nonostante la paura.

Non l'accompagno fino a sotto casa, ma vicino. Lei dice:

"Mia mamma non ci deve vedere insieme."

Adesso siamo soli, io e lei, le nostre mani una nell'altra, uno vicino all'altra. Avvicino le labbra alle sue e ci baciamo. È il primo vero bacio della mia vita.

"Ti voglio tanto bene" mi dice lei in un orecchio.

"Anch'io" rispondo.

13
In camera di Betta

Quando torno a casa, Betta non c'è.

"Betta sta via tutta la sera?" chiedo alla mamma.

"Sì, credo di sì. Come sempre. Io non ho niente in contrario, però frequenta certa gente…"

"Quale gente?"

"Gente… che non mi piace. Brutte facce! Comunque io non le dico più niente. Se le parlo dei suoi «amici» lei si arrabbia."

" Il papà dov'è?" chiedo io.

"Stasera ha una cena di lavoro…"

"Ma papà ha sempre le cene di lavoro?" domanda mio fratello Filippo. Una volta tanto ha ragione. È possibile? Papà non è mai a casa?

Sono le nove. Il piano superiore dove ci sono le camere da letto (mia, dei miei, di mio fratello e di Betta) è silenzioso. Mamma e le sue amiche giocano a bridge in salotto, mio fratello dorme, Betta è via, e io....

Entro nella sua camera. Conosco bene questa stanza. Ci sono stato migliaia di volte. So quindi dove guardare: apro i cassetti del tavolino. Ci sono tanti documenti, collane, dei disegni. Betta va a scuola di disegno. Li guardo: non sono belli come quelli di Sibilla!

Li rimetto nel cassetto… quando vedo che il fondo si muove. Scopro un sottofondo. Dentro: una sola cosa, una busta.

L'apro. E dentro trovo la fotografia, la fotografia di me in quella cantina!

"E adesso cosa vuoi fare?" È la voce di Betta. "Vuoi andare alla polizia, vero?"

Io la guardo. Ha una faccia dura e cattiva.

Non parlo, non dico niente e lei:

"Allora, mi rispondi?"

Perché ha questa voce? Perché nel suo sguardo leggo odio? Perché è stata complice[35] del mio rapimento?

Voglio chiederle tutte queste cose, ma sono così sconvolto che dalla mia bocca esce una sola parola: "Tu…"

"Sì, io!"

"Perché?"

"Perché io in questa casa ho sempre fatto una vita da serva. Da poveretta… Betta fai questo, Betta fai quello…"

"Ma tu… tu sei per me come una sorella, per i miei genitori come una figlia."

"Sì, una figlia che deve lavorare!"

"Ma a me sembra… io, la mamma, Filippo… ti vogliamo bene" insisto io. Non parlo neppure di papà, perché lui non mostra amore per nessuno.

"Ma per voi rimango sempre la figlia di serie B[36]!"

Io la guardo dritto negli occhi e dico con sincerità:

"Ma io no, io ti ho voluto veramente bene, Betta."

"Anche adesso? Adesso che hai scoperto…?"

Io non rispondo alla sua domanda, ne faccio un'altra invece:

---

[35] *complice:* una persona che aiuta altre persone a fare qualcosa (in genere di brutto).

[36] *di serie B:* che conta meno degli altri figli. L'espressione viene dallo sport del calcio, dove esiste la serie A (dove giocano le squadre più forti) e la serie B (dove giocano quelle meno importanti).

"È per questo mi hai fatto rapire?"

"Io non ti ho fatto rapire…"

"Cosa vuoi dire?"

"Non è venuta a me l'idea di rapirti. Anzi io non volevo."

"E allora chi?"

"A… a…" esita "io non posso dirti niente, assolutamente niente. Come non posso dire niente alla polizia. Tu non hai idea… Se parlo, quelli mi ammazzano."

"Non voglio andare alla polizia."

"E perché?" È stupita.

"Te l'ho già detto. Per me sei come una sorella."

"Non ti capisco. Non sei arrabbiato con me?"

Ci penso un attimo, poi rispondo:

"Sì. Tu hai fatto una cosa terribile. Ma… non devi andare in prigione."

Qualche secondo di silenzio.

"Se non vai alla polizia, ti prometto che lascio questa casa per sempre. Domani stesso."

"Dove vuoi andare?"

"Non lo so. Faccio le valigie e parto. Vado lontano. In Messico, in Brasile, sì in Brasile ho sempre voluto vedere il Brasile. Ho dei soldi in banca. Posso rifarmi una vita. Sono giovane."

Io non parlo, penso ai rapitori. Penso a quello che ha detto Beniamino: "Non puoi continuare a vivere nella paura. Devi sapere chi ti ha rapito."

Devo assolutamente scoprire chi sono e Betta è l'unica persona che mi può aiutare.

"Betta, io ora torno in camera mia e tu domani te ne vai via, ma prima devi dirmi una cosa."

"So che cosa vuoi sapere, ma io non te lo posso dire. Io non posso dirti chi sono loro. Non adesso."

"Perché?"

"Quella gente è pericolosa, Riccardo. Molto pericolosa."

"Betta, sai che hanno tentato di investirmi con la macchina?"

"Quando?"

"Circa un mese fa… "

Betta sta zitta per qualche secondo.

"Domani ti lascio sulla scrivania in camera un foglio. Lì trovi i nomi dei due uomini che ti hanno rapito."

Lascio la stanza. Non l'abbraccio e lei non abbraccia me. Ci salutiamo come due estranei.

La mattina dopo, molto presto, Betta va via.

Io vado nella sua camera. Trovo il foglio con i due nomi e una sola parola: *Perdonami*.

È domenica, i miei genitori si alzano tardi.

Soltanto alle undici mamma scopre che Betta ha fatto le valigie ed è andata via. Chiama papà. Sono senza parole.

"Io so perché" dico ai miei genitori.

"Cosa sai?" chiede papà.

"So molte cose e vi posso spiegare. Però promettetemi una cosa: non dovete fare niente contro Betta."

"Cosa significa?" domanda papà severo.

Papà si arrabbia, mamma anche. Ma io sono deciso. Non devono fare niente contro Betta.

Alla fine promettono e io comincio a raccontare. Tutto. Del mio primo incontro con Beniamino davanti al museo, delle ricerche del cugino di Max, dell'incidente e della scoperta del sacchetto del panettiere nella macchina di Betta. I miei ascoltano tutto silenziosi.

Quando finisco la prima domanda di mio padre è:

"Dove sono i nomi?"

Prendo il foglio dalla tasca dei jeans che indosso.

"Eccoli" e glielo do.

Lui legge i due nomi:

"Flavio Parenti… Marco Veronesi… Flavio… Flavio… questo nome mi è familiare…"

"Flavio Parenti" ripete mamma.

"Ma sì!" dice papà. "È stato il nostro giardiniere d'estate. Due o tre anni fa."

"La polizia ha detto che i rapitori sono spesso persone che conoscono la casa…" aggiunge mamma.

"Già, purtroppo. Come Betta…" dice papà.

"Ricordati quello che hai promesso su Betta!" intervengo io.

"Sì, lo ricordo, per ora non ne parliamo. Anche se non capisco perché vuoi proteggere una persona che ti ha fatto del male."

"Perché le voglio bene" rispondo io semplicemente.

Poi mia mamma chiede:

"Perché in tutto questo tempo non ci hai detto niente? Perché hai parlato con tutti, persino con un barbone, ma non con noi, perché?"

Già, perché? Io lo so, ma non lo dico. I miei genitori devono capirlo da soli. Perciò rispondo: "Non lo so."

14
La fine

Mio padre telefona alla polizia che arresta i due uomini il giorno stesso e perquisisce il loro appartamento, ma non trova niente.

"Neppure la più piccola prova" dice il commissario "niente di niente. Se non mi dite chi vi ha dato queste informazioni, oppure se non trovate il testimone, domani mattina quegli uomini sono fuori."

"Allora?" mi dice mio padre. "Adesso dobbiamo trovare Betta!"

"Betta è lontana " rispondo io.

"C'è sempre Beniamino. Lui è il nostro testimone."

"Non so se accetta di testimoniare…"

"Se accetta di testimoniare? Ma quante storie…" papà è molto arrabbiato adesso. "*Deve* testimoniare."

"No, lui non deve niente. Beniamino è … è…" non so come dire "un uomo giusto."

"Ah, un uomo giusto… ma se è un barbone! E poi, se non vuole avere a che fare con la polizia, deve essere lui stesso un criminale."

"Beniamino è una brava persona. Ed è un amico. E adesso vado a cercarlo, da solo."

"No."

"E allora non faccio niente."

"Riccardo, guardami! Io sono tuo padre."

E a quel punto esplodo:

"Mio padre, mio padre… Ma se non ci sei mai… non ci sei a cena, non ci sei nei week-end, o, se sei in casa, sei sempre impegnato con il lavoro e con i tuoi amici. Quand'è l'ultima volta che abbiamo parlato io e te? Non mi ricordo. Forse non è mai successo. E Filippo che chiede sempre di te? Perché mio fratello ha ancora bisogno di un padre."

Lui non risponde. Dopo qualche secondo dice soltanto:

"Ho capito. Se vuoi andare da solo, vai. Io ti aspetto a casa."

Sono quasi le sette. Vado diritto alla mensa della chiesa dei Francescani. Beniamino deve essere lì e infatti lo trovo. Il mio amico sembra contento di vedermi, anche se subito fa una faccia preoccupata.

"Non preoccuparti" gli dico io. "I rapitori sono in prigione."

Lui smette di mangiare la sua zuppa e andiamo in un bar a prendere un panino. Qui gli spiego tutto e alla fine gli chiedo di venire a testimoniare.

"Va bene, lo faccio" dice lui.

"Grazie, Beniamino."

"Prima devo dirti una cosa importante. Devo parlarti di una cosa che ha a che fare con il mio passato e con… la polizia."

Beniamino mi racconta una storia:

"È la storia di un professore. Insegna storia e filosofia in un liceo. Qui in città. La materia e il suo lavoro gli piacciono molto. Sta bene con i ragazzi. Non è sposato né fidanzato… è un tipo solitario, lo è sempre stato. Lavora in una scuola «difficile» dove ci sono molti ragazzi con problemi di famiglia. Alcuni si drogano. Lui li aiuta. Un giorno due poliziotti vanno a casa sua. Dicono che vende droga. Perquisiscono il suo appartamento, ma non trovano niente. Però ci sono due testimoni. Queste due persone dicono che il professore vende droga. Lui risponde che non è vero. Ma non gli credono. «Possiamo arrestarla» dice il commissario «ma, se va via da scuola, può restare libero. Però, naturalmente non può più insegnare.» Il professore ci pensa e poi risponde: «Sì, va bene.» A scuola, del resto, sanno tutti quello che è successo, e credono alle accuse di quei due."

"Il professore sei tu, vero?"

"Già."

"Ma perché quei due hanno detto che vendevi droga?"

"Perché io aiutavo i ragazzi drogati, ero diventato un problema per chi vendeva droga. In questo modo ero fuori. Per sempre. Dopo un mese ero a casa, solo, senza amici, senza lavoro, senza soldi. Così, dopo un anno, sono rimasto anche senza casa."

"Povero Beniamino!" penso.

"Tu mi credi, vero?" chiede lui.

"Certo che ti credo! Io so che sei un uomo buono e onesto."

"Grazie, Riccardo."

Beniamino va alla polizia per testimoniare. Così i rapitori rimangono in prigione e i poliziotti possono continuare a indagare. Perquisiscono le automobili e i garage dei due. Qui trovano le chiavi della porta della cantina e la maschera.

I miei due rapitori hanno trent'anni. Nessuno dei due ha mai avuto un lavoro fisso, ma non sono mai stati in prigione prima.

"Adesso vanno in prigione" dice il commissario a me e a mio padre. "E ci stanno per un bel po' di tempo!"

Una sera parlo a lungo con mio padre. La più lunga conversazione della mia vita con lui, "da uomo a uomo".

È una sera di febbraio, esattamente il quattordici febbraio, il giorno di San Valentino. Io vorrei essere con Sibilla a festeggiarlo. Invece oggi non l'ho neppure vista.

Oggi finisce per sempre la mia storia di rapito. Mai più paura, mai più rapitori o pericoli...

Sono con papà nel suo studio. Questa stanza fa parte di casa nostra, ma io non ci entro mai. È una specie di stanza segreta di papà.

"Devo dire che sei stato molto bravo. Sono orgoglioso di te" dice papà.

"Grazie" rispondo io e non so cosa altro dire. Però questo complimento da parte di papà mi fa piacere.

"È brutto che tu non ci abbia detto niente, a me e alla mamma. Anche se capisco..."

Non sa bene come continuare. Mio padre, che sembra sempre sicuro di sé, adesso sembra imbarazzato.

"Io capisco che... sì insomma... in questi anni sono stato troppo poco presente, ma devi capire anche tu, io ho una grossa azienda che devo mandare avanti, affari importanti."

"Sì, lo capisco papà."

"No, non lo capisci" adesso grida "tu non lo capisci, perché alla tua età queste cose non si capiscono. Si è pronti a giudicare, ma non a capire."

Fa di nuovo una pausa. Mi guarda.

"Io dico solo che a me sembra di non avere neppure un padre" rispondo io. "Tu sei sempre fuori, io non ti vedo mai. Se ho bisogno, non posso parlarti perché sei occupato. Io non ti giudico, ti dico soltanto come stanno le cose per me."

Gli ho già detto queste cose, ma di nuovo sembra avvilito[37].

---

[37] *avvilito:* demoralizzato, triste.

43

"Io penso di non essere stato un cattivo padre" dice "io cerco soltanto di darvi il meglio. Ti prometto che da ora in poi sarò più presente."

Fa una pausa e poi riprende:

"Devo anche parlarti di un'altra cosa molto importante, Riccardo. Il commissario mi ha detto una cosa sul tuo amico Beniamino."

"Sì, so tutto" rispondo io.

"Io voglio lo stesso parlarti di questo, perché forse tu pensi di continuare a frequentare quell'uomo…"

Mi dice che Beniamino è un ex professore e che ha lasciato la scuola perché vendeva droga. Mi dà anche degli articoli di giornale di allora.

"Guardali, leggili" mi dice.

Poi mi saluta con un abbraccio. Un vero abbraccio.

Da solo nella mia camera leggo tutto. È come mi ha raccontato il mio amico. Ma non credo a quello che c'è scritto. Invece credo a lui.

Io so che è innocente, so che è un uomo buono e onesto, e rimarrò suo amico, per sempre.

ATTIVITÀ

Parte 1 - Capitoli 1-2-3

1. Indica quali di queste affermazioni sono vere o false.

		vero	falso
a.	Riccardo è solo.	❏	❏
b.	L'uomo che entra nella stanza gli porta da mangiare.	❏	❏
c.	L'uomo è molto brutto.	❏	❏
d.	Riccardo ha paura.	❏	❏
e.	Riccardo passa il tempo guardando fuori dalla finestra.	❏	❏
f.	Riccardo legge sui giornali la storia di Giannetto.	❏	❏
g.	L'uomo torna e fa una fotografia a Riccardo.	❏	❏
h.	Riccardo mangia molto.	❏	❏

2. Com'è la "prigione" di Riccardo? Completa.

La stanza è .... e .... Nella stanza c'è soltanto un .... L'unica finestra è coperta da .... Nell'altra stanza, per terra, Riccardo vede un .... e una pila di ....

3. Riccardo ricorda il suo rapimento. Ricostruisci la storia rispondendo a queste domande.

a. Dove si trova Riccardo?   c. Chi lo rapisce?
b. Che cosa sta facendo?   d. Perché?

4. Riccardo pensa molto alla sua famiglia e ai suoi amici. Trova le informazioni e riportale qui di seguito.

• suo fratello:...
• il suo amico:...

5. Rispondi a queste domande sul terzo capitolo.

a. Cosa fa Riccardo per arrivare alla finestrella?
b. Che cosa vede dalla finestrella?

c. Alla fine la polizia lo "salva". Chi ha (probabilmente) chiamato la polizia?

6. *Barbone* è una parola molto importante nella storia. Cosa vuol dire in italiano?

a. persona con una grande barba. ❑

b. persona che non ha dimora ovvero una casa fissa. ❑

c. persona che viaggia continuamente. ❑

7. Trova nel testo parole per dire:

a. negozio in cui si compra il pane ....

b. animale roditore ....

c. notizia scritta su un giornale ....

8. Qual è la parola sinonimo di *stupido*?

Parte 2 · Capitoli 4-5-6

1. Indica la giusta alternativa.

1. La storia riprende. Sono passati	a. due mesi
	b. due anni
	c. due giorni
2. Riccardo ha spesso	a. bei sogni
	b. incubi
	c. brutti pensieri
3. Riccardo va sempre	a. dalla psicologa
	b. a scuola
	c. dal suo amico Max
4. A scuola adesso Riccardo è	a. molto popolare
	b. antipatico a tutti
	c. un ragazzo come gli altri
5. Riccardo	a. vuole essere più libero
	b. ha ancora paura
	c. ha dimenticato tutto

6. Max è
   a. uno dei tanti amici
      di Riccardo
   b. il miglior amico di Riccardo
   c. semplicemente un compagno
      di scuola di Riccardo

7. Max pensa tanto
   a. alla scuola
   b. alla famiglia
   c. alle ragazze

8. Durante la gita al museo Riccardo
   vede
   a. delle cose interessanti
   b. il barbone
   c. la sua amica Sibilla

9. Riccardo vuole un favore
   a. dal cugino di Max
   b. da Max
   c. dalla sua insegnante

10. Sibilla deve
   a. scrivere un tema sui ricordi
   b. fare un identikit di Max
   c. fare un identikit del barbone

2. Sottolinea gli elementi falsi nella descrizione di Sibilla.

È una vicina di casa di Riccardo. È molto bella, ma antipatica. Ha i capelli lunghi e biondi. Le piacciono le storie d'amore e vede tanti film di fantascienza.

3. Adesso rispondi a queste domande sul ruolo che gioca il cugino di Max nella storia.

1. Perché va a casa di Riccardo di sera?
2. Che cosa gli dà Riccardo?
3. Che cosa gli dà il cugino di Max a sua volta qualche giorno dopo?

4. Collega l'espressione con il giusto equivalente.

1. grida come un'aquila   a. tutti sono concentrati su di lui
2. ha una fame da lupi   b. pensa solo a…
3. ha in testa solo (le donne)   c. parla ad altissima voce
4. adesso è al centro dell'attenzione   d. è molto affamato

5. Quale parola non c'entra con le altre?

a. bocca	b. naso	c. orecchio	d. piede
a. cugino	b. madre	c. padre	d. amico
a. western	b. interessante	c. d'amore (sentimentale)	d. fantascienza
a. tetto	b. camera	c. corridoio	d. stanza
a. jeans	b. gambe	c. maglione	d. maglietta

6. Trova nel testo i sinonimi di

a. denaro (bigliettoni) ....
b. insegnante ....
c. molto carino ....

7. Quali di questi sono nomi di dolci in italiano?

❏ a. crostata ❏ d. lasagne
❏ b. cotoletta ❏ e. macedonia
❏ c. tiramisù ❏ f. salame di cioccolato

Parte 3 - Capitoli 7-8-9

1. Rispondi alle seguenti domande riguardo al primo capitolo.

1. Dove trova Riccardo il barbone?
2. Che cosa fanno insieme?
3. Di che cosa ha paura Riccardo? E il barbone?
4. Dove torna Riccardo e con quale mezzo?

2. Adesso indica quali di queste affermazioni (riguardo ai capitoli 2 e 3) sono vere o false.

	vero	falso
a. Riccardo ha cambiato "look" e la mamma ne è molto contenta.	❏	❏
b. Sibilla non parla con Riccardo perché è offesa con lui.	❏	❏
c. Max è molto bravo a scuola.	❏	❏

d. La domenica Riccardo va a una festa di un suo compagno di classe.	❏	❏
e. Alla festa si annoia.	❏	❏
f. Va a cercare Beniamino e lo trova.	❏	❏
g. Insieme vanno a mangiare.	❏	❏
h. Riccardo parla molto della sua vita.	❏	❏

3. Il barbone diventa un personaggio importante nella storia. Cosa sappiamo fino a questo momento di lui? Completa la descrizione.

È di .... statura. Ha i capelli .... e la barba. Va a mangiare nella .... dei frati francescani e di notte dorme nel .... Parla come un .... E forse lo è stato.

4. Riccardo si chiede "perché cerca la compagnia del barbone", ma non sa darsi la risposta. Perché secondo te?

5. Riccardo parla di suo padre. Che cosa dice riguardo a lui?

6. Collega l'aggettivo della colonna a destra con il suo contrario nella colonna a sinistra.

economico	lontano
sciocco	disinvolto
vuoto	difficile
triste	intelligente
facile	costoso
imbarazzato	felice
vicino	pieno

7. Quali di queste parole appartengono all'ambito del "sentimento (amore) e relazioni sentimentali"?

❏ innamorarsi ❏ amore ❏ moglie
❏ azienda ❏ scuola ❏ insegnante
❏ fidanzato ❏ relazione ❏ appuntamento

8. **Dove si fanno queste cose? Abbina il nome del luogo con l'attività che si svolge.**

ristorante	visitare
dormitorio	divertirsi
scuola	mangiare
festa	dormire
museo	imparare

9. **Al ristorante Riccardo e Beniamino mangiano una volta la "pizza quattro stagioni" e la "seconda volta "pasta e fagioli". Conosci queste specialità italiane? Ti piacciono? Parla in classe di altri piatti tipicamente italiani.**

Parte 4 - Capitoli 10-11-12

1. **Indica la giusta alternativa.**

1. Beniamino non parla mai a lungo al telefono perché
   a. ha poco tempo
   b. ha pochi soldi
   c. non ha voglia di parlare con Riccardo

2. Dopo un mese
   a. non si hanno notizie dei criminali
   b. Beniamino ha smesso di cercare
   c. Max esce con Sibilla

3. Quando Betta accompagna Riccardo a casa di Max, Riccardo trova nella sua macchina
   a. i soldi del riscatto
   b. la foto dei rapinatori
   c. il sacchetto del panettiere con la scritta Stelladi

4. Riccardo racconta a Sibilla di questa scoperta, poi si baciano
   a. nel bar
   b. sotto casa di Max
   c. vicino a casa di Sibilla

2. Adesso rispondi a queste domande riguardo al capitolo 2.

1. Di sera Riccardo decide di perquisire la camera di Betta. Qui trova qualcosa che indica che Betta in effetti ha a che fare con il suo rapimento. Che cosa?
2. Perché Betta non vuole dire i nomi dei rapinatori?
3. Perché Riccardo non dice nulla ai suoi genitori di Betta e la lascia andare?

3. Completa il seguente riassunto del capitolo 3.

Il commissario dice che hanno trovato i ...., ma non possono tenerli in prigione perché non hanno nessuna ....
Perciò l'unico che può fare qualcosa è Beniamino. Lui infatti .... Dopo una discussione con suo padre, Riccardo va a cercarlo e gli chiede di .... Lui accetta, e poi gli racconta la sua storia.
Riccardo crede che Beniamino sia innocente.

4. Di che cosa accusa Riccardo suo padre?

5. Sai raccontare brevemente la storia di Beniamino con parole tue?

6. Ti piace la fine della storia? Perché?

7. In questo capitolo compaiono alcune parole che hanno a che fare con il crimine: *arrestare, perquisire, testimoniare.*

1. *Arrestare* significa
   a. far smettere qualcuno di fare qualcosa
   b. portare qualcuno in prigione
   c. interrogare qualcuno

2. *Perquisire* vuol dire
   a. cercare qualcuno in un certo posto
   b. cercare qualcosa in modo accurato e metodico in un certo posto
   c. analizzare le prove

3. *Testimoniare* si usa quando qualcuno
   a. dice quello che ha visto o sentito davanti alla polizia e in un processo
   b. è presente sul luogo del delitto
   c. interroga qualcun altro

8. Quali di queste sono materie scolastiche? Sottolinea.

storia	simmetria
scienze	cinema
corpo umano	italiano
filosofia	matematica
geografia	gastronomia

CHIAVI

Parte 1 - Capitoli 1-2-3

1. 1. a. vero; b. vero; c. falso; d. vero; e. falso; f. vero; g. vero; h. falso.

2. brutta e vuota; letto; sbarre; water; giornali.

3. a. Si trova in un campo di calcio. b. Sta giocando a pallone. c. Degli uomini mascherati d. probabilmente perché la famiglia di Riccardo è ricca e vogliono chiedere il riscatto.

4. Il fratello di Riccardo si chiama Filippo ed ha quattro anni meno di lui. Max è il migliore amico di Riccardo, è un tipo strano, molto popolare tra i ragazzi, poco tra i genitori perché corre dietro alle ragazze.

5. a. mette il letto sotto la finestrella e la pila di giornali sul letto così riesce a guardare fuori b. Vede un cortile con due bidoni della spazzatura c. Probabilmente il barbone.

6. b.

7. a. panettiere; b. topo; c. articolo.

8. idiota.

Parte 2 - Capitoli 4-5-6

1. 1-a; 2-b; 3-b; 4-c; 5-b; 6-b; 7-c; 8-b; 9-a; 10-c.

2. è una vicina di casa di Riccardo; è antipatica; ha i capelli biondi; le piacciono le storie d'amore.

3. Per prendere il ritratto (identikit) del barbone. Gli dà trecento euro in una busta. Gli dà delle informazioni su dove può trovare il barbone.

4. 1-c; 2-d; 3-b; 4-a.

5. piede; amico; interessante; tetto; gambe.

6. a. soldi; b. professore/professoressa; c. bello.

7. crostata, tiramisù, salame di cioccolato.

Parte 3 - Capitoli 7-8-9

1. 1. Riccardo trova il barbone alla mensa dei frati francescani. 2. Vanno a mangiare in un ristorante. 3. Riccardo ha paura che lo possano rapire di nuovo/di essere rapito di nuovo. Il barbone ha paura che lo uccidano se sanno che è stato lui a telefonare alla polizia. 4. Riccardo torna a casa di Max in taxi.

2. a. falso; b. falso; c. falso; d. vero; e. vero; f. vero; g. vero; h.vero.

3. media; grigi e lunghi; mensa; dormitorio; professore.

4. Perché si sente solo e non sa con chi parlare di sé e della sua esperienza.

5. che lavora molto e non è molto presente nella vita familiare.

6. economico/costoso; sciocco/intelligente; vuoto/pieno; triste/felice; facile-difficile; imbarazzato-disinvolto; vicino-lontano.

7. innamorarsi; amore; moglie; fidanzato; relazione; appuntamento.

8. ristorante-mangiare; dormitorio-dormire; scuola-imparare; festa-divertirsi; museo-visitare.

Parte 4 - Capitoli 10-11-12

1. 1-b; 2-a; 3-c; 4-c.

2. 1. La foto di lui nella cantina (di quando è stato rapito). 2. Perché ha paura di loro. 3. Perché le vuole ancora bene.

3. rapinatori; prova; è un testimone; testimoniare.

4. Riccardo lo accusa di essere un padre poco attento.

7. 1-b; 2-b; 3-a.

8. Storia; scienze; filosofia; geografia; italiano; matematica.

Note

Note

Note

L'italiano per stranieri

Ambroso e Di Giovanni
L'ABC dei piccoli

Ambroso e Stefancich
Parole
10 percorsi nel lessico italiano
esercizi guidati

Anelli
Tante ide...
per (far) apprendere l'italiano

Avitabile
Italian for the English-speaking

Balboni
GrammaGiochi
per giocare con la grammatica

Barki e Diadori
Pro e contro
conversare e argomentare in italiano
- **1** livello intermedio - libro dello studente
- **2** livello intermedio-avanzato - libro dello studente
- guida per l'insegnante

Barreca, Cogliandro e Murgia
Palestra italiana
esercizi di grammatica
livello elementare/pre-intermedio

Battaglia
Grammatica italiana per stranieri

Battaglia
Gramática italiana para estudiantes de habla española

Battaglia
Leggiamo e conversiamo
letture italiane con esercizi per la conversazione

Battaglia e Varsi
Parole e immagini
corso elementare di lingua italiana
per principianti

Bettoni e Vicentini
Passeggiate italiane
lezioni di italiano - livello avanzato

Blok-Boas, Materassi e Vedder
Letture in corso
corso di lettura di italiano
- **1** livello elementare e intermedio
- **2** livello avanzato e accademico

Buttaroni
Letteratura al naturale
autori italiani contemporanei
con attività di analisi linguistica

Camalich e Temperini
Un mare di parole
letture ed esercizi di lessico italiano

Carresi, Chiarenza e Frollano
L'italiano all'Opera
attività linguistiche attraverso 15 arie famose

Chiappini e De Filippo
Un giorno in Italia 1
corso di italiano per stranieri
principianti · elementare · intermedio
- libro dello studente con esercizi + cd audio
- libro dello studente con esercizi (senza cd audio)
- guida per l'insegnante + test di verifica
- glossario in 4 lingue + chiavi degli esercizi

Chiappini e De Filippo
Un giorno in Italia 2
corso di italiano per stranieri
intermedio · avanzato
- libro dello studente con esercizi + cd audio
- libro dello studente con esercizi (senza cd audio)
- guida per l'insegnante + test di verifica + chiavi

Cini
Strategie di scrittura
quaderno di scrittura - livello intermedio

Deon, Francini e Talamo
Amor di Roma
Roma nella letteratura italiana del Novecento
testi con attività di comprensione
livello intermedio-avanzato

Diadori
Senza parole
100 gesti degli italiani

du Bessé
PerCORSO GUIDAto - *guida di* **Roma**
con attività ed esercizi

du Bessé
PerCORSO GUIDAto - *guida di* **Firenze**
con attività ed esercizi

du Bessé
PerCORSO GUIDAto - *guida di* **Venezia**
con attività ed esercizi

Gruppo CSC
Buon appetito!
tra lingua italiana e cucina regionale

Gruppo META
Uno
corso comunicativo di italiano - primo livello
• libro dello studente
• libro degli esercizi e grammatica
• guida per l'insegnante
• 2 audiocassette / libro studente
• 1 audiocassetta / libro esercizi

Gruppo META
Due
corso comunicativo di italiano - secondo livello
• libro dello studente
• libro degli esercizi e grammatica
• guida per l'insegnante
• 3 audiocassette / libro studente
• 1 audiocassetta / libro esercizi

Gruppo NAVILE
Dire, fare, capire
l'italiano come seconda lingua
• libro dello studente
• guida per l'insegnante
• 1 cd audio

Istruzioni per l'uso dell'italiano in classe 1
88 suggerimenti didattici
per attività comunicative

Istruzioni per l'uso dell'italiano in classe 2
111 suggerimenti didattici
per attività comunicative

Istruzioni per l'uso dell'italiano in classe 3
22 giochi da tavolo

Jones e Marmini
Comunicando s'impara
esperienze comunicative
• libro dello studente
• libro dell'insegnante

Maffei e Spagnesi
Ascoltami!
22 situazioni comunicative
• manuale di lavoro
• 2 audiocassette

Marmini e Vicentini
Passeggiate italiane
lezioni di italiano - livello intermedio

Marmini e Vicentini
Ascoltare dal vivo
materiale di ascolto - livello intermedio
• quaderno dello studente
• libro dell'insegnante
• 3 cd audio

Paganini
issimo
quaderno di scrittura - livello avanzato

Pontesilli
Verbi italiani
modelli di coniugazione

Quaderno IT - n. 4
esame per la certificazione dell'italiano come L2
livello avanzato - prove del 2000 e del 2001
• volume + audiocassetta

Quaderno IT - n. 5
esame per la certificazione dell'italiano come L2
livello avanzato - prove del 2002 e del 2003
• volume + cd audio

Radicchi
Corso di lingua italiana
livello intermedio

Radicchi
In Italia
modi di dire ed espressioni idiomatiche

Stefancich
Cose d'Italia
tra lingua e cultura

Stefancich
Quante storie!
(di autori italiani contemporanei)
con proposte didattiche

Stefancich
Tracce di animali
nella lingua italiana
tra lingua e cultura

Svolacchia e Kaunzner
Suoni, accento e intonazione
corso di ascolto e pronuncia
• manuale
• set 5 cd audio

Tamponi
Italiano a modello 1
dalla letteratura alla scrittura
livello elementare e intermedio

Tettamanti e Talini
Foto parlanti
immagini, lingua e cultura

Ulisse
Faccia a faccia
attività comunicative
livello elementare-intermedio

Urbani
Le forme del verbo italiano

Verri Menzel
La bottega dell'italiano
antologia di scrittori italiani del Novecento

Linguaggi settoriali

Ballarin e Begotti
Destinazione Italia
l'italiano per operatori turistici
• manuale di lavoro
• 1 audiocassetta

Cherubini
L'italiano per gli affari
corso comunicativo di lingua e cultura
aziendale
• manuale di lavoro
• 1 audiocassetta

Dica 33
il linguaggio della medicina
• libro dello studente
• guida per l'insegnante
• 1 cd audio

L'arte del costruire
• libro dello studente
• guida per l'insegnante

Una lingua in pretura
il linguaggio del diritto
• libro dello studente
• guida per l'insegnante
• 1 cd audio

Pubblicazioni di glottodidattica

Gabriele Pallotti - A.I.P.I. Associazione Interculturale Polo Interetnico
Imparare e insegnare l'italiano come seconda lingua
• DVD + libro

Progetto ITALS

La formazione di base del docente...
a cura di Dolci e Celentin

L'italiano nel mondo
a cura di Balboni e Santipolo

Cedils. Certificazione in didattica...
a cura di Serragiotto

Il 'lettore' di italiano all'estero
a cura di Pavan

ITALS. Dieci anni di formazione e ricerca
a cura di Balboni, Dolci, Serragiotto

I libri dell'Arco

1. Balboni • **Didattica dell'italiano a stranieri**

2. Diadori • **L'italiano televisivo**

3. Micheli • **Test d'ingresso di italiano per stranieri**

4. Benucci • **La grammatica nell'insegnamento dell'italiano a stranieri**

5. AA.VV. • **Curricolo d'italiano per stranieri**

6. Coveri, Benucci, Diadori • **Le varietà dell'italiano**

Classici italiani per stranieri

testi con parafrasi a fronte* e note

1. Leopardi • *Poesie**
2. Boccaccio • *Cinque novelle**
3. Machiavelli • *Il principe**
4. Foscolo • *Sepolcri e sonetti**
5. Pirandello • *Così è (se vi pare)*
6. D'Annunzio • *Poesie**
7. D'Annunzio • *Novelle*
8. Verga • *Novelle*
9. Pascoli • *Poesie**
10. Manzoni • *Inni, odi e cori**
11. Petrarca • *Poesie**
12. Dante • *Inferno**
13. Dante • *Purgatorio**
14. Dante • *Paradiso**
15. Goldoni • *La locandiera*
16. Svevo • *Una burla riuscita*

Libretti d'Opera per stranieri

testi con parafrasi a fronte* e note

1. *La Traviata**
2. *Cavalleria rusticana**
3. *Rigoletto**
4. *La Bohème**
5. *Il barbiere di Siviglia**
6. *Tosca**
7. *Le nozze di Figaro*
8. *Don Giovanni*
9. *Così fan tutte*
10. *Otello**

Letture italiane per stranieri

1. Marretta
Pronto, commissario...? 1
16 racconti gialli con soluzione
ed esercizi per la comprensione del testo

2. Marretta
Pronto, commissario...? 2

16 racconti gialli con soluzione
ed esercizi per la comprensione del testo

3. Marretta
Elementare, commissario!
8 racconti gialli con soluzione
ed esercizi per la comprensione del testo

Mosaico italiano

racconti italiani su 4 livelli

1. Santoni • *La straniera* - liv. 2
2. Nabboli • *Una spiaggia rischiosa* - liv. 1
3. Nencini • *Giallo a Cortina* - liv. 2
4. Nencini • *Il mistero del quadro di Porta Portese* - liv. 3
5. Santoni • *Primavera a Roma* - liv. 1
6. Castellazzo • *Premio letterario* - liv. 4
7. Andres • *Due estati a Siena* - liv. 3
8. Nabboli • *Due storie* - liv. 1
9. Santoni • *Ferie pericolose* - liv. 3
10. Andres • *Margherita e gli altri* - liv. 2 e 3
11. Medaglia • *Il mondo di Giulietta* - liv. 2
12. Caburlotto • *Hacker per caso* - liv. 4
13. Brivio • *Rapito!* - liv. 1

www.bonacci.it

Bonacci editore

Finito d stampare nel mese di settembre 2007 dalla Tibergraph s.r.l. - Città di Castello (PG)

How to
Lose Weight
and be Healthy

A Guide to the Art of Eating

Harish Chavda

GW00566149

Published by Holistic Health Publishing

DISCLAIMER

This book is to provide general information only and should not be treated as a substitute for the medical advice of your doctor or any other health care professional. Always consult your doctor if you are in any way concerned about your health.

ISBN: 978-0-9574798-0-7

Design and Typesetting by:
Roxbourne Press Ltd, Harrow Middlesex HA2 9SE

Cover Image © Carlo Giunta.

Table of Contents

Chapter 1

—

INTRODUCTION

"Let food be your medicine" ~ *Hippocrates*

INTRODUCTION

Welcome to the little book with the power to make big changes to YOUR life!

Why this book is essential for YOU

Perhaps you are someone who wants to diet, tone up, or just adopt a healthier way of living. Maybe you are even someone who has a health issue that you believe is related to your diet and the way you eat. Or perhaps you are someone who is so caught up in the *fast lane* that you even forget to eat.

Whatever your reason for selecting this book, one thing is certain: this book is not another fad diet book. Nor does it make any false claims about having some miracle cure. This book offers an alternative solution by providing the answers to a different question by addressing *how to eat* rather than *what to eat*.

You are not just what you eat – you are how you eat

We are about to delve into the wonderful world of the forgotten art of eating. If you are skipping this fundamental step in life, then it could be the reason why you are suffering with many ailments. Those who do not eat in the correct manner may find that they experience:

- Obesity
- Exhaustion and fatigue
- Digestive disorders
- Bad skin, nails or hair
- Eating disorders

Whatever your ailment, through reading this book and correcting *how* you eat rather than *what* you eat, you will find an overall improvement in your health that some would call nothing short of 'miraculous'. What you are about to discover here is very simple but extremely effective.

My own journey of self-discovery

At one stage of my life, my daily routine involved sitting at a desk in an office staring at a computer screen for long periods of time, sometimes up to twelve hours a day. There was little room for physical movement and very little fresh air. I was plagued by stress, which affected my mental and physical health. I experienced extremely low energy levels and found it difficult to sleep. My enthusiasm for life was at a very low level.

My struggles with back and weight problems

Due to work pressure I found myself working long hours, which resulted in me spending less time looking after my health, weight and fitness. My weight fluctuated like a yo-yo. I often found myself skipping a meal, eating too much and eating at the wrong time. Mid-day lunch involved eating at my desk, *mouse in one hand and sandwich in the other while surfing the Internet.* Lunch usually lasted between ten and fifteen minutes. I was also suffering from various digestive issues such as constipation, irritable bowl syndrome (IBS), stomach pains and tiredness. Working in a stressful office environment, coupled with a lack of exercise and a sedentary life style, all contributed to my weight and digestion problems.

When I developed a serious back condition I sought the advice of a medical practitioner, only to be told the devastating news that it was possible that I would not be able to walk again. Visits to chiropractor and osteopath offered temporary relief, but the benefits soon wore off. However, I refused simply to give up and took matters into my own hands.

Yoga, meditation and exercise improved my life

I changed my lifestyle. I took up yoga. Yoga improved everything that was out of balance, as it worked on my breathing and posture. My back began to heal itself and my physical strength and stamina reached levels I once thought impossible. Practicing yoga led me to learn how to breathe properly and relax through meditation. This also helped me to slow down and handle the stress of daily life better, especially in my working environment. I also started to exercise by taking up cycling, running, and playing racquet sports such as squash and badminton.

Yoga and physical exercise, however, was just a partial solution to my health issues. I was still suffering from low energy, digestion and weight problems. I tried conventional medicine but it only offered temporary relief. I was looking for a permanent solution that was natural and had no side effects. The answer came from an unexpected source: my eighty-year old father.

The importance of my father

My father was a man who had never really suffered with any medical problems during his long life. Whilst eating with him one day I noticed how he would eat his food in a certain way. I saw that he was at peace while eating. He would eat his food and thoroughly chew it. He took his time to eat slowly and relish every bite. I spent more and more time eating with him, noting how he breathed and how relaxed he always seemed. I was sure that there had to be a connection between his relaxed and meticulous way of eating and his physical wellbeing.

The missing link – The Art of Eating re-discovered

Researching the connection between breathing, relaxation and eating, I discovered that how you eat as well as what you eat will have a direct impact on your health. I started practicing what I had discovered by changing how I ate my food.

- I now take time to eat food slowly
- I chew my food thoroughly

- I eat food with awareness
- I use natural methods to boost my digestion
- And I practice meticulous eating habits

By practicing the above my health improved dramatically. I no longer suffered from low energy and digestive problems and I was now maintaining my ideal weight. I had regained my health and vitality. Where once doctors had suggested that I would not be able to walk again I now found myself partaking in multiple challenges for charity. Since then I have climbed mountains – Mount Kilimanjaro in Africa (16,000 ft) and the three highest mountains in the United Kingdom: Ben Nevis (4409 ft), Scafell Pike (3209 ft), Snowdon (3560 ft) - run several marathons (26 miles) and cycled from London to Paris (300 miles). If I can do it – so can you!

Why I wrote the book

I resolved to help others to achieve the sort of health that I had achieved and so I started the Art of Eating Project. The project aims to empower people by giving them the knowledge to achieve a healthier and happier lifestyle and I now run educational courses and seminars on the Art of Eating and Stress-Free Living.

Through the means of this book I aim to share with a wider audience the secrets that I have discovered. I will show you how you can unlock the door to better health simply by focusing on *how you eat*.

Be prepared for dramatic changes to your health. Remember, I know this will work for you because it has worked for me.

This book is not a diet book!

There are plenty of those already on the market.

This book goes right back to basics and looks at the importance of *how to eat* rather than *what to eat*. You may be someone who has tried every possible diet that you can think of but nothing seemed to work in quite the way that you hoped it would. Well, I think I know why. The other diets failed because you have not been informed of the *missing vital step* that needs to be put into action *even before you take a mouthful of food*. Therefore, regardless of what plan you choose to follow or what lifestyle you adopt, all of your efforts could be going to waste if you are not correcting *how* you eat.

The key is the **Art of Eating** – how you eat the food that you choose to eat. It is vital that you address this area before investing any more time, energy or money in what you put into your body. We will cover the following topics:

- Our eating habits – what has gone wrong?
- The science behind eating – How the digestive system works.
- How to eat – preparation, environment, act of eating and after eating.
- The importance of chewing food.
- Tips on good eating habits.

This book will help you to look at the bad habits that you have formed throughout your lifetime but will also help you to understand why and correct them. It will guide you through the art of eating in a straightforward easy to read layout. There is no need to feel overwhelmed. The journey that you are about to undertake should be the most natural journey in the world and may feel a little like an awakening.

Chapter 2

THE FORGOTTEN ART OF EATING

THE FORGOTTEN ART OF EATING

What exactly has gone wrong?

It is true that most of us have lost touch with life. We have forgotten how to live *in the moment*. We ignore the essence and the power of paying attention to what we do in the present. As a result, we find ourselves running through our busy lives on autopilot and at frightening speed. The resulting negative effects on our general health and our natural relationship with food are extremely destructive. Below are the key points that look at what exactly has gone wrong and why so many of us are suffering in so many different ways.

Modern living – life in the fast lane

We are a generation driven by speed. Fast living, fast food, fast everything. And this rushed pace of life means that many of us don't take enough time to eat our food properly, or in some cases, we skip meals. It seems that everything today in our society has to be done at speed – even the process of eating! Have you thought it strange that we have time for shopping, work, watching television , social activities, holidays but when it comes to eating, which is the key to our well being and actual survival, we don't have time. We are now under such pressure at home and at work that some of us spend less than forty minutes a day eating. How are we supposed to thrive physically and professionally if we have a lack of vital nutrients and energy?

Overeating (The Obesity Time Bomb)

A sedentary lifestyle and overindulgence in junk food is creating a generation who will grow up prone to heart disease, diabetes and cancer. Eating too much food does our digestive system and overall health no favours at all. This point is confirmed by the wealth of information we continue to hear and read detailing government concerns and medical research about obesity problems in our society.

We have become like machines

Once immersed in the fast pace of life, we begin to run on autopilot. We become almost machine-like. Our routines are so precise that we become automated and we lose touch with our natural balance. Through creating and adhering to such rigid mechanical routines, we have become totally out of step with the laws of nature. We follow the clock rather than the sunrise and sunset. Our bodies are out of step with the universal energy. We are humans, not machines, and our first step must be to look at how we can get out of the fast lane.

Emotions

Whilst pushing ourselves to the limit, we may find ourselves unbalanced and stress, depression and insomnia can all affect our relationship with food. For example, many people comfort eat, rather than slow down and tackle the real problem.

Multi-tasking

If and when we do find time to eat during our fast-paced lives, it is often in the form of fast food grabbed while doing something else in order to convince ourselves that we are being efficient. Multi-tasking while eating diverts our attention from our food, leading us to eat more than we really need. For example, *a computer mouse in one hand and a sandwich in the other, while surfing the Internet at lunchtime*, like I did for about ten years, is not good for anyone. Make a firm rule that you will not surf the

Internet, talk on the phone, read a newspaper, watch television or do anything else when you are in the process of eating.

Not living in the present

In order to connect with eating we need to be focused in the present moment and on the task at hand. But how is this possible when we are constantly distracted and always thinking about the past or the future?

No physical exercise

Today, physical activity is a very small part of our daily lives and it's all too easy to neglect exercise. How can we expect to burn off excess calories or feel in great shape and condition and get our metabolisms functioning if we are inactive?

We don't use our five senses whilst eating

Food could, and indeed should, be a multi-sensory, enjoyable and creative experience. If we are disconnected from the present moment and distracted by our fast-paced life and by multi-tasking, how can we engage our senses fully with the food that we eat?

Why are we always tired?

In order to feel energized, we need food, the body's fuel. And once we eat this food, we need to digest it in the correct manner so that we can absorb all of the nutrients as effectively as possible. Forgetting to eat, overeating or eating in a hurried manner, gives rise to overall poor digestion and thus poor health. Forgetting to eat altogether means that we are simply running on empty! Taking time out to eat and to eat properly is the key to beating fatigue. In the modern world, we eat too much food and the body uses an enormous amount of energy to digest it; energy that could be used more efficiently elsewhere.

Bad eating habits

Skipping lunch for one busy day soon turns into two and three and, before we know it, we are developing a pattern of bad eating habits. It is so easy to operate on automatic when it comes to food. Living in a fast-paced society often forces you to eat on the run, skip meals and eat whatever is fast and easy. Some people find it is easier to eat late at night while others eat large portions in order to relieve stress. It generally takes around 21 days to make or break a habit and so we need to go right back to basics and teach ourselves how to eat.

The effects of bad eating habits on our health

Bad eating habits are common throughout all classes of society and obesity, bad skin, hair loss, stress and depression are just a few of the side effects. Without the nutrients that it requires, the body simply cannot survive. *Choose to thrive rather than simply to survive.*

We eat with machines!

We used to eat as a family at the dining table, Sunday lunch used to be a regular activity but now eating seems no longer to be a social activity in the home. Now we eat while watching television, working or playing on the computer or smart phone. Our attention is focused on the machine instead of our food. By failing to pay attention to our food and the actual process of eating we are leaving ourselves open to the trap of overeating and the danger of obesity.

Eating disorders (a modern day illness)

Conditions such as anorexia and bulimia are on the increase in today's fast-paced, high-pressured society. In order to prevent or alleviate these extreme results of an unbalanced mind and body, we must learn to see food not only as necessary fuel for the body to develop and thrive but also importantly as an enjoyable experience.

Chapter 3

THE SCIENCE BEHIND EATING

> *"Take care of your body. It's the only place you have to live"* ~Jim Rohn

THE SCIENCE BEHIND EATING

How the body works

Eating is a basic function that we are not *taught* to do – it is just something that every child instinctively knows how to do from birth. However, in our modern age, as soon as we start eating for ourselves, we appear to have lost this understanding of *how* to eat.

You could buy the most wonderfully healthy pure organic food that is available but, if you are not eating and digesting it in the correct fashion, then a great deal of its goodness will simply be excreted from your body and disposed of as waste. Have you ever stopped to think about this? Every single mouthful you put into your mouth is packed with vital nutrients, which can only be absorbed properly if the food is digested in a certain way.

When your body is not getting the nutrients that it needs your entire system suffers. Health issues that affect both the mind and the body will develop and you may end up taking a great deal of time off work as a result. You may also find yourself taking medication for ailments that can simply be corrected by addressing the basics. Wouldn't life be a lot easier if you knew how to begin the correct eating process?

Back to basics

The first step in unravelling the cycle of bad habits is to go right back to basics.

If you take away all of the clutter, the act of eating can be divided into two basic categories:

1. The actual *need* for food – we need food as fuel for survival. In addition we need good food if we are to be in the best possible health.
2. The *function* of food – its digestion, the absorption of nutrients, plus the elimination of waste.

What you eat today walks and talks tomorrow...

Food is much more than a basic need or function. If we go without it for more than 30 days we die! But food is not simply the fuel for life. There is nothing simple about the process of converting digested food into the fuel or nutrients that your body needs. And the way in which we eat our food greatly alters how our body can use it.

There is an Art to how we eat it and this affects the way in which the food is digested and in turn what the body can absorb and eliminate for optimum health.

So many people simply shovel their food in – the faster the better – that a lot of those essential nutrients are lost because the body cannot process them properly. So that, while we think that we are adhering to a good diet and may be the world's most fantastic cook, all our efforts could be wasted through the simple act of eating in the wrong way.

If digestion is compromised and we do not absorb the correct nutrients then our overall health suffers. When we lack energy, our skin, hair, nails, teeth and other places in our body and mind show signs of deficiency. The body becomes out of balance and illnesses occur.

Though the wrong food, the wrong sort of diet and bad lifestyle choices, all create ill health, I have some good news. We *can* change things and use *how we eat* and *what we eat* as a form of medicine. Food is a wonderful natural healer if you know which ingredients to use for which ailment. Perhaps you have tried a 'juice fast' in order to detox your body, or perhaps you have switched to an organic diet or cut down on the amount of red meat you consume each week? But what happens if you go through all of this effort only to destroy the hard work by failing to alter the *way* you eat? Or worse, you undo all the good by simply lapsing into bad habits again?

How the digestive system works

This amazing, mechanical system, which includes the oesophagus, stomach, intestine, bowel, and a whole host of enzymes and processes, is responsible for processing the food that you eat. Your digestive system sorts out the nutrients you do need from the waste that you don't need. However, in order for it to do its job to its best ability, the digestive system needs a little support from you. You can do this by making sure that the food that you introduce into your body is not only properly nutritious but is also eaten in the correct manner.

Let's take a moment to look at digestion, so that you can gain a better understanding of how the body works and why it is so important for the food to be in its desired state (which it arrives at via eating it in a certain way) before it begins the digestion process.

There are three key processes involved in digestion of your food.

1. The Digestion Process, which breaks down food into molecules.
2. The Absorption Process, which absorbs nutrients into the blood, which carries them through the body.
3. The Elimination Process, which discharges the waste matter.

Digestion - a complex journey

What happens to your food once it has been swallowed? Well, it depends upon several factors: it can be processed, absorbed and used for energy and health or it can be rejected and expelled as toxins or waste.

Digestion is an energy consuming activity and so the more that you can do to help break the food down *before* it reaches your stomach the less stress and pressure that is put on your system. For example when your stomach muscles are relaxed they can work more efficiently.

Digestion begins in the mouth. Food is mixed with digestive juices so that it can be swallowed with ease and passed through the stomach until it finally reaches its destination, which is the small intestine.

The digestive system is not as scary as you may think! It simply comprises of:

- Mouth
- Teeth
- Tongue
- Salivary glands
- Oesophagus
- Stomach
- Small intestine
- Large intestine

Figure 1 shows the main parts of the digestive system.

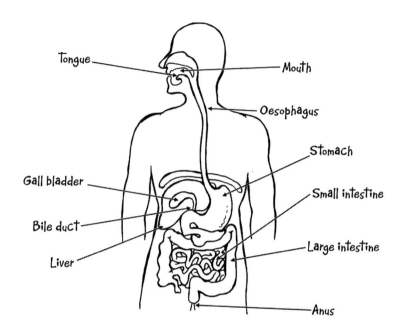

Figure 1 Digestive system

Let's take a look at what actually happens to food when it is in any of these given areas.

Mouth: The mouth is where the digestion process begins. The mouth consists of three parts that all work together to break the food down: the teeth, the tongue and the salivary glands. From the very first bite of food the teeth begin the digestive process as they break the food down into smaller pieces and then these parts are mixed with saliva so that the food can pass down from the mouth into the oesophagus with greater ease. It is recommended that each mouthful of food remains in the mouth for 15 seconds in order for this activity to take place.

Teeth: On average, human beings have 32 teeth in their mouths and these play a crucial role in grinding the food down into digestible pieces in preparation for swallowing. The teeth are necessary for mastication – the process by which we tear, cut and grind food in preparation for swallowing. Chewing then allows enzymes and lubricants released in the mouth to further digest or break down the food.

Tongue: The tongue is a muscular organ that sits comfortably in the mouth and works in two main ways in regard to food and digestion. Firstly, it contains taste buds that enable us to determine whether a food is hot, salty, spicy, sweet or bitter. Secondly, it helps push the food along on its journey, assisting it to leave the mouth with ease.

Salivary glands: These are situated in the wall and floor of the mouth and secrete saliva which acts as a lubricant to help break the food down as much as possible before it continues on its journey. It also contains enzymes that aid in the digestion of carbohydrates, such as bread, pasta or rice.

Oesophagus: Located in your throat, close to the trachea (windpipe), the oesophagus is where food arrives after being passed along via the mouth. Here it is pushed further by a series of wave like muscle contractions and food is delivered to the stomach in only two seconds.

Stomach: Once the food arrives in the stomach it is mixed with acid and enzymes. The stomach is lined with glands that produce digestive juices and acid that not only helps break the food down into a liquid pulp but also neutralizes any bacteria that may have found its way into the stomach. During a two to four hour process the food is digested and then pushed along towards the small intestine.

Small intestine: The small intestine is the main site of human digestion and is where all of those vital nutrients are processed and absorbed. The pancreas, liver and gall bladder secrete a combination of enzymes, chemicals and bile, which all help the food to pass along smoothly. The inner wall of the small intestine is lined with tissue whose cells extract nutrients from the food, which are then passed into the bloodstream. Whilst all of this intricate digestion is taking place, food that has been dealt with is then passed along into the large intestine. On average, food remains in the small intestine for six hours.

Large Intestine: Anything that was not absorbed to be used within the body in the small intestine then reaches the large intestine. Here any water or nutrients that can be extracted are re-absorbed before the rest of the matter is sent along to the rectum to be dispelled as waste from the anus in the form of faeces. This absorption and elimination process can take as long as 14 hours.

The whole digestive system is about nine metres long and in a healthy human adult body the full digestion process can take between 24 and 72 hours.

The mind and body connection

Your body reacts to the way you think, feel and act. This is often called the 'mind and body connection'. Your thoughts and emotions affect your body as surely as the food you eat.

The mind is extremely powerful. It has the positive potential to cure illness and yet, on the other hand, it can also encourage disease and can be incredibly destructive. The mind plays an important role in eating. Did you know that where eating is concerned 80% is in the mind, involving the five senses, and only 20% is in the physical act of eating?

1. The mind and body connection helps us decide which foods we like and don't like. It works to enable us to decide which foods we desire when we are out shopping in the supermarket.
2. The mind and body connection has the ability to process information and help us decide which foods are good and bad for us.
3. The mind tells us when to eat. The body may send signals such as a rumbling stomach and the mind learns to recognize that as hunger.

Not only does the mind work out all of the above but it also controls our digestion and how much food we eat.

Stress and the mind and body connection

It is at the subconscious level that the mind has its greatest influence on our bodies. This can mean that we react to events in our lives in different ways. Some situations and events cause positive emotions and some cause negative emotions. Our bodies react in different ways to the stresses we feel. Thoughts and emotions trigger chemical responses in the body. Positive thoughts lead to the release of brain chemicals that make us feel good. Negative thoughts and emotions release chemicals that can make us feel bad and may lead to health problems. The list of these problems is long but the most well known are those affecting the heart and stomach.

The mind and body connection varies between people and the physical manifestations vary greatly. A well known example is that of two people who go through exactly the same experience but have very different reactions to the experience, with one person feeling little or no distress while the other person feels traumatised. It is important to learn how to deal with the many types of stresses in life in order to strengthen your emotional and physical health. Traditional medicine and alternative healing have never really gone hand in hand but many doctors today recommend alternative therapies such as meditation, yoga, relaxation and visualisation techniques in order to deal with health problems.

The relationship between relaxation and the Art of Eating

With the modern problem of living life in the fast lane, scheduling time out for much needed relaxation can often feel like 'mission impossible'. Aside from the time factor, many of us struggle with the outdated mind-set passed on from previous generations ('work hard, play hard') that taking time for yourself is often considered 'selfish'.

We are all made up of energy and, if our tanks are running on empty, how can we expect to give anything more to our career, our partner, our family or our friends?

Topping up our energy tanks on a daily basis is a little like charging a mobile phone: we cannot expect our phone to continue to function unless it is regularly plugged into a source of power in order to re-charge it!

A lack of relaxation can lead to a build-up of side effects such as stress, tension, muscle pain, headaches, insomnia and, in serious cases, depression. Blood pressure can be affected and, at worst, a heart attack or stroke could be on the horizon.

Your digestive system is often affected by stress and stress is an amazing appetite suppressant. A lack of relaxation can affect your eating patterns dramatically. A lack of appetite leads to skipping meals and this then feeds a vicious cycle as not eating wholesome food triggers other ailments and issues.

Therefore, the relationship between relaxation and *how you eat* is both undeniable and extremely important. Most of us realise that it would be good for us to step out of the fast lane and spend more time in the slow lane. In a similar way to the Art of Eating, the Art of Relaxation is a basic but vital step essential for survival. If we miss relaxation out of our daily routine then everything else will be out of harmony.

As you are about to discover, the Art of Eating requires that you approach mealtime in a calm and relaxed manner. Great emphasis is placed upon consuming your food at a steady pace. When we are stressed we find it difficult to leave our worries behind and focus on the task at hand and it is all too common for food to be gulped down, which then leads to indigestion and other health issues.

A little later in this book we will look at tips and ideas as to how you can slot some easy everyday relaxation techniques into your busy schedule, in order to not only work on your whole self but, specifically, to enhance your journey and relationship with food and the Art of Eating.

Key points to remember

Digestion begins before eating: Sitting in a restaurant looking at the menu will have your appetite building before you even see the food, thus firing up your salivary glands to produce saliva.

Food is partially digested in the mouth: The enzyme breaks down carbohydrates (bread, rice, pasta) into smaller molecules in the mouth.

Chewing: If you do not take proper care to chew sufficiently then your food will sit in the stomach and will be harder to break down and digest.

Emotional state: Mind plays a key role in the process of digestion. So try to eat food when you are in a calm and relaxed state.

Taste: Chewing your food for a little longer means that you will taste your food properly as your taste buds will have time to savour it.

—

Chapter 4

HOW TO EAT CORRECTLY

"You are how you eat" ~Harish Chavda

HOW TO EAT CORRECTLY

There are three main areas to consider when we look at how to eat correctly:

1. **The process before you eat** – preparation of food and your eating environment.
2. **The act of eating** – how to eat.
3. **The process after you eat** – rest period for the body so that it can digest the food that has been eaten.

We will look at each area in more detail but, before we do that, it is important to focus on one major factor that is often overlooked: the importance of YOU. Before you address anything else, stop and consider how you are presenting yourself.

If you are distracted or stressed then this will manifest itself in your physical body. You may find your stomach feels tense, you may experience frequent loss of appetite or you approach your meal with a sense of urgency and a tightening of the throat – none of which are conducive to a healthy eating experience

Therefore, the first step is to focus on yourself and look at how you can relax and make sure that your body is working most efficiently, so that you gain the most nutrients from your meal while you are eating.

The key ingredient to the Art of Eating is relaxation. Add to that a dash of time, creativity and awareness and you have the right environment both externally and internally in which to move forward and make real changes that will benefit your health and every area of your life.

Get out of the fast lane!

There are ways that you can prepare yourself before eating such as hand washing, which may contribute to an altered state of mind, thus breaking the rhythm of the fast lane and entering the sacred space that is the slow lane.

If at all possible, try to include a short relaxation exercise into your daily routine. It can be as simple as a five minute meditation or ten deep breaths but carrying this out just before approaching the eating area will help to leave the worries of the day behind you. You can then be on your way with your preparation.

1. The process before you eat

Be aware of the importance of preparation. Preparation covers everything from choosing what you are going to eat to creating the perfect space within which to eat it. Make this a fun part of the journey and unleash your creative juices.

If you approach your preparation, including shopping for food, in an unbalanced or over-emotional state, then you are more likely to buy foods that you can binge on or buy more than you need for one meal. When approaching the Art of Eating, your mind-set is extremely important.

Choose healthy wholesome foods that appeal to your senses. Notice the colour, the texture and the smell of your ingredients. The food that you put into your body is the fuel for life. So, before focusing on *how you eat*, address *what you eat* and appreciate the medicinal benefits that food can have. You have the power to heal your body with the choices you make when you go shopping to buy food.

Preparation is not just exclusive to ingredients. It is also relevant to the area within which you will cook your food and the area where you will eat it. Make sure that the space is clean, de-cluttered and has all of the utensils that you will need in one space. You want to step out of the fast lane, so you don't want to have to rummage around for tools and utensils, as this will leave you feeling stressed and frustrated.

Mental preparation is a vital step before commencing cooking and eating. However, this is, of course, easier said than done. You want to leave the world outside behind you, and enter into a sacred, happy and tranquil space as this will help with the Art of Eating and digestion. As mentioned earlier, try to slot something like meditation or a breathing exercise for just five minutes before tackling anything else: before you start cooking or before you sit down to eat.

Hand washing, as I mentioned earlier, is something that we can all do. It does not have to be just a case of basic hygiene, it can be a way of preparing you for a pleasurable experience. Alternatively, you could perhaps take a little walk around the garden or simply sit comfortably, close your eyes and breathe in and out deeply, being aware of your breath.

Prepare a meal fit for a king

Be creative

Enjoy preparing and cooking your food and think of it as an art form. You are the creator and your plate will contain your masterpiece.

Make sure that you present your finished creation as though you were presenting it to an audience. Be aware of how you lay your table, what size plate you use, the cutlery that suits you best and the comfort of your chosen dining area.

Be aware of portion control as overeating is something that is all too easy to do and many people fill a plate that is far too big for them. Choose a smaller plate and always remember that it is better to start off with a smaller amount. You can always go back for seconds if you are still hungry!

Show gratitude

When you sit down ready to tuck into your feast show gratitude for the food that you are about to eat. Think about all the people whose hard work and effort brought the food to the table, from the farmer to the supermarket to the cook. Again this acts as a mental trigger: it helps you to breathe, slow down and connect to the act of eating while focused in the present moment. You may like to incorporate this into your daily routine and, of course, you can adapt it according to your chosen religion or spiritual practice.

2. The act of eating

Being focused in the present and being mindful of the here and now is how you are then able to connect with the food that is on your plate. Before you simply begin to shovel it into your mouth, sit back and allow your senses to engage with your creation.

Take a moment to look at what lies on the dining table before you and engage with all of your senses. Savour the aroma and allow your appetite to be triggered. This will get your saliva flowing which, as you now know, is the first step required for digestion. Allow your mind and body to become aware that eating and digestion is about to begin.

How to eat

When you are born you know how to eat. You just do it by instinct. There is no book or workshop required and you are not taught how to suckle on your mother's breast or take milk from the bottle. Living in the fast lane we have picked up bad eating habits and forgotten our natural instincts to eat correctly.

Learn how to eat slowly, with awareness. How often do you actually notice the look, feel, taste and smell of your food? Stepping back and slowing down is the key to enjoying food.

Would it now surprise you if I told you that there are actually seven important steps involved when it comes to the art of eating and they need to be followed in sequence in order for optimal digestion and health to exist?

Let's look at those seven steps one by one:

Seven steps to the Art of Eating

Step One: Look at the food (Sight)

Look at your food and express gratitude and appreciate what you have before you. Think of your food on the plate as being the end result, a piece of art that has been created. Take a moment to marvel at it. Think of all the steps that had to be made in order to get things to this stage. Look at the wonderful items that have been cooked, noticing the colours and the textures. Let your saliva buds begin to awaken.

Step Two: Smell the aroma of the food (Smell)

Take time to smell the food. You may bend down a little as you look at this wonderful creation and inhale the aroma, perhaps summing up in a sentence what it is that you can smell, such as 'it smells really meaty/fruity/spicy'.

Step Three: Pick up the food (Touch)

Pick up the food. You may use your hands or other cutlery. Close your eyes as you take your first mouthful as this helps you to focus on the sensation in the mouth. Now open your eyes, what does the food feel like? Feel with your tongue and palate the texture and notice whether it is hot, warm or cold.

Step Four: Taste the food in your mouth (Taste)

Don't be in a rush to gulp it down. Really take time over noticing the mixture of flavours and allow your taste buds to come alive.

Step Five: Chew the food (Sound)

Slowly chew the food in your mouth. Does it crunch when you chew? Notice the sound as your food groups mix together.

Step Six: Ingest the food (Swallow)

By now you will have stimulated your salivary glands to such an extent that your food will have been processed, nicely mixed with enzymes, and is in a desirable state for you to swallow it.

Step Seven: Relax (Breathe)

It is typical for most people to shovel another forkful into the mouth as soon as one mouthful has been swallowed. Just take a moment. Relax and take a deep breath as you become aware of the sensation of your food as it passes down into your stomach.

Repeat the cycle all over again, going back to step one.

Do you notice how this process revolves around the senses, patience and relaxation? Not only will slowing down whilst eating aid better digestion but it will also give you time out from your busy schedule so that you can relax a little. By practising the Art of Eating you are recharging your batteries. For example, rather than stressing about taking time out of your working day, think of it as an excellent time frame within which you can reconnect to the natural you and gain extra power, so that you work even more effectively and efficiently in the afternoon than you did in the morning.

The Seven steps to the Art of Eating are illustrated in Figure 2.

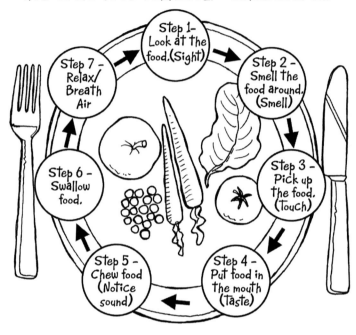

Figure 2 How to eat correctly - The Seven Steps

Drinking while eating

It is acceptable to drink a small amount of liquid while eating but you need to be aware that liquid dilutes the stomach acid and digestive enzymes, making them less effective at breaking down food. It is best to drink liquids before eating or two hours after eating in order to help uptake of nutrients and to aid bowel movements.

Pause between bites

One final point to mention is not to have food in your hand or on your fork whilst you are eating a mouthful. If possible place your fork down on your plate and focus all your energy on the act of eating. This will help you resist putting another forkful into your mouth before you have properly digested the previous one.

3. The process after you eat

Congratulations! You have taken time to savour every mouthful, chewing correctly and allowing your body to begin the process of digestion in a gentle and relaxed manner. Now, the worst thing you could do after finishing your meal would be to jump up from the table and be physically active.

Just as you took time out to move gently into the slow lane, so you should give yourself a time frame within which to allow digestion to take place before rushing back into the fast lane.

Thinking of meal time as a ritual, why not take a little more time to give thanks for the food that you have just eaten? Wash your hands again in order to send a message to the brain that the act of eating has finished. Just as you opened the activity so you are now able to close it.

Although relaxation right after a meal is promoted, do try not to go to sleep for a little while. It is important to healthy digestion that you do not eat too close to bedtime. This brings us to the importance of routine and timing. Planning roughly when you are going to have your meals ensures that you receive a steady and balanced intake of food and thus have the fuel for the daily output of energy. This helps to keep energy levels constant and ward off fatigue. It also maintains a stable blood sugar level.

Breakfast

Just as you want your body to be in a relaxed state and not digesting food during the night time you will need to be sure to have breakfast upon waking no matter how small you make it. The word breakfast can be split into two halves *break* and *fast*. The idea is that you break the fast that you have taken during the night and 'kick-start' your metabolism for the day that awaits you. It is most important that you do not skip breakfast. It has often been called 'the most important meal of the day'.

Ideally you should be getting 25 percent of the day's calories from breakfast, enough to keep you going right through until lunchtime, both physically and mentally. Starting the day without refuelling the body's engines may well result in poor concentration, irritability, low blood sugar and a dreadful craving for that biscuit or chocolate bar in the middle of the morning.

Lunch

For one week try to make your lunch last longer than usual. If you usually take five minutes to eat a sandwich, try to take 15. Then build this up to 20, 25 and 30. Get used to savouring every mouthful and take note of how you feel physically after learning to slow down a little. I guarantee that you will no longer have that 'full-up' feeling. Your energy level in the afternoon will be better than you could ever imagine. Try it!

Eating with awareness

Slow eating is about eating with awareness. As we have already asked how often do you actually notice the look, feel, taste and smell of your food? Stepping back and slowing down is the key to enjoying food.

EXERCISE

Consider for a moment how would you eat an apple. Think about this now for a moment; imagine that you have just been handed an apple. What would be your natural instinct upon receiving the apple in your hand? Be honest! Most people would probably be taking that first bite before they even realize that they are doing so.

Now imagine that you are holding the apple in your hand. You may like to close your eyes if this helps visualization. What does the apple feel like? Is it cold, dry, slippery, hard? Put the apple to your nose and inhale. Does it have an aroma?

There is no catch to this and you can try this at home right now if you happen to have an apple handy. Notice how you eat. Do not try and implement the teachings of this book but eat it as you would normally eat it. Make a mental note of how you eat this apple and how you feel right after. Do you chew it properly? Do you hold the apple in your hand as you chew wanting to take the next bite as soon as possible or do you put it down and allow yourself time to digest that first mouthful before proceeding?

It is a very simple exercise, but really gets to the heart of the matter. Slow eating is not just about chewing and swallowing but taking time out and creating space within which you will prepare not only your meal but also your mind-set in order to physically eat your food in a calm and healthy way.

Chapter 5

THE ART OF RELAXATION

THE ART OF RELAXATION

Relaxation is something that is recommended throughout this book. It helps you to slow down, get out of the fast lane and focus on the present moment. This then helps you to engage your five senses with the food that you are about to prepare and eat and will enable you to give your undivided attention to each and every mouthful as you concentrate on taking your time and eating your food properly.

But if you are someone who leads an extremely busy life, perhaps because of your work or family obligations, it is not that easy to slow down when you have no choice but to enter the fast-paced environment that is your everyday life style.

Many people find the idea of leading a stress free relaxed pace of life difficult simply because they cannot realistically envisage just how they will find the time and energy to invest in relaxation. Learning to relax is not difficult - it just needs time and practice. Experts recommend setting aside at least 10 to 20 minutes a day for relaxation practice. Here are some of the relaxation techniques you can try:

- Deep breathing
- Visualization
- Meditation
- Listening to music
- Yoga
- Exercise
- Massage therapy

Even the busiest person can practice some of these techniques in the office or in the home environment.

Three simple practices that will change your life:

1. Planning your day into hourly slots
2. Five minute break
3. One hour lunch break

1. Planning your day into hourly slots

By focusing on one hour at a time we are directing our vision and thoughts and not jumping too far ahead into the future, worrying about things that may never happen.

By planning your day and then looking at each hour as a segment of that day, everything seems less overwhelming. You are then able to channel your energy into the task at hand and not worry about what else needs to be done during that day, as you have it all covered.

EXERCISE

Plan your day by using a journal, writing down each hour and then filling that hour with an activity. Even if you plan to sit and watch television for two hours or talk on the phone for one hour, pencil it in.

Make sure that in this daily journal you allocate sufficient time for three meals a day. This will help you to relax. In general, you will have less stress and fewer racing thoughts. You will find that, as you get used to planning your day into hourly slots, that you become more and more focused on the present moment at any given time. When you operate within a short time frame (one hour), you will find that the bigger picture that at first overwhelmed you becomes smaller and more manageable.

2. Five minute break

Within each hour schedule yourself a five-minute break.

Try to spend the last five minutes of every hour during your working day on a mini-break, a time when you rest your mind. The key is to stop and focus on something different. Ideally you should move away from your work environment. You may wish to do some quick exercise, go for walk or simply grab a cup of coffee. Alternatively, you may just do some deep breathing exercises.

Now your initial reaction to this, especially if you are someone who works hard during the day and lives life in the fast lane, might well be that taking five minutes out of every hour slows down your output and therefore affects your daily productivity rate. If you work eight hours a day for instance, you might well think that devoting what would be 40 minutes on relaxation would be a waste of valuable time.

But think about this: how often do you find yourself unable to come up with a solution to a problem because of a mental block brought about by stress? By insisting that we charge through each day on a fast speed setting we are not necessarily putting our best self forward. The old saying that 'quality versus quantity' applies perfectly to the scenario above. Believe it or not, you will find that if you take more mini-breaks you can actually accomplish *more* in the day.

When you run yourself ragged and insist on multi-tasking you may physically feel as if you are working hard and putting your all into whatever it is that you are working on. But if your energy tanks are running low, or are close to empty, how efficient are you really?

By slotting a five-minute mental break into every hour you will experience the following positive benefits:

1. The satisfaction of acknowledging all that you have created during the hour that is coming to an end.

2. The enthusiasm for all that you are about to experience and create for the hour that you are about to enter.

3. A refreshed mind-set, so that you are able to work in short bursts with renewed energy, rather than feeling as if your day is one long slog.

4. An overall improved sense of relaxation throughout the course of any given day.

You are able to break your day down into bite size, digestible chunks and zoom through every hour knowing that all you are tackling at any given time is a 55 minute time frame. You will then give yourself permission to take a five-minute break before tackling the next hour. This practice, combined with dividing your daily schedule into hourly slots, will slow your pace right down - because you are in control of what needs to be done and when.

3. One hour lunch break

If you have a daily job, what is your lunch break like? Do you carry on with your work while you eat a quick sandwich? It seems that most working people do just that – only one in six take a proper lunch break and, when they do, it lasts less than 30 minutes. And then they wonder why they lose concentration, become stressed and their energy levels decrease.

There are so many benefits in taking a full hour lunch break. You will have time to recharge your batteries and be able to step back and focus more clearly on your work. You will discover that you are able to manage stress better and boost your energy levels and concentration. If you do not want simply to sit and eat for the full hour go out for a walk, listen to music, meditate or read a book but *do not sit in front of your computer*!

If you follow these three practices, which work in harmony with your daily eating plan, you may benefit from the following:

1. You will be more relaxed, so your digestive system will be rested and ready for you to digest your food.

2. You will have a healthy sense of balance to your life and your appetite will no longer suffer undue stress.

3. As you wind down at the end of the hour prior to taking your lunch break, you will be able to get yourself into eating mode and begin to gear your mind-set to the task at hand.

4. These practices will keep your system steady and balanced so that there is less temptation to rush through your afternoon and interfere with the digestion and absorption of the food that you have just consumed.

How to relax

Relaxation is the key to a balanced equilibrium and general sense of oneself. Once you master this art you will find that you are able to approach the *Art of Eating* with a greater mental clarity and engage your five senses fully.

Here is an example of how you could use your five-minute break. It works in a similar way to a guided meditation or a visualization exercise. You can, of course, choose your own scenario. The little exercise below has been created to keep you calm and focused and help you to develop a greater sense of awareness.

EXERCISE

Wherever you are, whatever you are doing, just stop for a moment. Place your hands in your lap and, if at all possible, close your eyes. Relax your shoulders and allow any stored tension to melt away.

Imagine that there is a golden ball of healing energy swirling above you. It gently floats down and begins to swirl around you. Feel the warm and tingly energy as it begins to enter your body. It starts at the top of your head and works its way down into your facial muscles, down across your shoulders and all the way down to the tips of your fingers.

Imagine this energy as it trickles through your body, filling every single part of you, until it finally reaches your toes. Wiggle your toes once the energy is there and focus on the weight of your feet in your shoes.

You are deeply relaxed.

Now imagine that you are on a beautiful sandy beach. You can hear the sound of the waves as they gently lap on the shore. Perhaps you can hear some children playing nearby or maybe you prefer total silence? This is your beach and so you create your own perfect relaxing reality.

Feel the sand as you walk along the shore and look ahead as you see a beautiful carved rock.

Should you not wish to use the gratitude exercise I mentioned earlier, this exercise is great to practise just before eating. You can also do it after eating. It will instantly relax you and transform your day and, if you stick to this routine, your whole life.

It is an easy routine to follow and does not interfere with your busy schedule to any great extent. It is user friendly as you don't even have to leave your chair to do it, and it certainly takes up less time and effort than going for an hour or two to a relaxation class.

By adopting a routine such as this you will bring your body back into the here and now and will find that you are more aware of your biological rhythms.

It is a great way to exist in the fast lane without being sucked dry by it. Take some power back. If you do have to exist in that fast lane, create your alternative reality within that space.

Laughter, relaxation and weight loss

Laughter is a great way to relax and lose weight. You can watch comedy movies, television shows or read humorous books as a way to unwind and relax. It may even help you to lose weight. According to research carried out by Vanderbilt University in America, laughing 10-15 minutes a day would burn an extraordinary 2.2 kilograms a year. What a great way to lose weight! The old saying 'laughter is the best medicine' holds true, and has been verified by many studies.

Why not join a laughter yoga club?

Laughter yoga is a unique concept created by Dr Madan Kataria, a physician from Mumbai, India. Laughter yoga utilizes the breathing techniques of yoga coupled with group laughter that uses no comedy props. It combines laughter exercises with yogic breathing, which brings more oxygen to the body, thus making one feel more energetic and healthy. The concept is based on scientifically demonstrated fact that the body cannot differentiate between 'fake' and real laughter. A person will get the same mental and physical benefits. It is the finest antidote for stress relief and a great way to relax and lose weight! There are more than 6000 social laughter clubs in about 60 countries worldwide. Why not find out if there are any laughter clubs running around your local area?

Positive thinking

Positive thinking may help with stress management and can even improve your health. Practise overcoming negative self-talk. Use a positive thinking mind-set to change the way you feel. If you follow the adage 'live, love, laugh' and practise some of the relaxation exercises, it is undeniable that your health and well-being will improve.

Chapter 6

HEALTHY EATING HABITS

> *"First we form habits; then they form us. Conquer your bad habits or they will conquer you."* ~Robert Gilbert

HEALTHY EATING HABITS

When we were born we knew how to eat correctly. It just came naturally to us as if it was in our wiring. But then, as we grew up, bad habits became part of our reality and, in effect, took over our lives. However, our ability to eat correctly has never fully gone away; it just lies dormant.

What is a habit?

A single thought can lead to an action and, if this action is repeated over and over again, it can then become a habit. However, just as we have formed bad habits by the repetition of certain actions so we can replace those actions with a positive alternative. Bad habits take time to develop but, if we are willing to put in a little time and effort, they can be broken. One way to begin your journey to break these bad habits is to set yourself the 21 Day Challenge, as created by surgeon, Dr Maxwell Maltz.

21 Day Challenge

When an action is repeated over and over, the brain actually picks up on it and creates something called a 'neuron pathway' in response to the trail that this action leaves behind. This means that your action becomes embedded in your brain and that is why, after a little time, we can carry out habitual actions almost without thinking about them.

Just as we can hardwire or train our mind to absorb and remember an action, we can also re-train it. We cannot erase a habit as such but what we can do is replace it with a new one.

Create a new habit

In order to install a new habit into our brain we need to bombard it with information over 21 consecutive days so that the new data will be accepted. It is important not to miss a day. This scientific technique can therefore be applied to any of the techniques outlined in this book in order to develop a new habit. And, of course, this can work for multiple habits, although it is advised to try and focus on just one at a time. However, don't then abandon one as you attempt to work with a new habit. It is essential that you keep on practicing any that you focus on. Remember: use it or lose it.

Step by step

Always approach change one little step at a time. Drastic changes can be a shock to the system and the more you try to control everything and cut things out too quickly the more you crave your old ways.

This technique is wonderful because it also helps you to break the task down into bite size pieces and tackle one area at a time. The problem with many self-help books is that they flood the reader's mind with far too much information and the idea of change, although it is appealing, can often seem overwhelming and thus people tend to give up.

EXERCISE

1. Choose one area to focus on, such as portion control, quitting the working lunch or finding time every day to get out of the office environment to eat properly.

2. Perhaps write your desired new habit on a note and stick it in a place where you can be reminded of your goal over the course of the next 21 days.

3. Remain focused on achieving your goal and set yourself a reward for having completed it, such as a spa day, a weekend break or a night out with friends.

4. When 21 days are up, you can tick the achievement off on your calendar, feel proud of yourself for a while and then move onto the next habit.

By following the 21 Day Challenge, in conjunction with 10 tips that are outlined below, you will soon transform the way in which you eat.

Good Eating Tips

Tip 1:   Slow down.

Tip 2:   Follow Nature's Principles.

Tip 3:   Eat your food in the right environment.

Tip 4:   Use the right tools for eating.

Tip 5:   Don't let your emotions determine how you eat.

Tip 6:   Pay full attention to the act of eating.

Tip 7:   Chew your food thoroughly.

Tip 8:   Eat the right amount of food.

Tip 9:   Boost your digestion.

Tip 10: Relax after eating.

Write these ten good eating tips here on a piece of paper or photocopy the page and stick it to your refrigerator or, better still, create a place mat and keep it on your table so that you will remind yourself of these handy tips during each meal time.

Chapter 7

—

TIP ONE
SLOW DOWN

GET OUT OF THE FAST LANE!

> *"There is more to life than increasing its speed"' ~Mahatma Gandhi*

TIP ONE - SLOW DOWN

The number one problem with living life in the fast lane is that meal times are often skipped, forgotten altogether or, when eating actually does take place, indigestion is often experienced afterwards due to a rushed and stressed way of eating. This can have a knock-on effect on our overall health. We try to cram more and more into each 24 hour day. Endlessly invented technology, which is supposed to save us time and enjoy our leisure, is, in fact, making our lives ever more fast-paced. Mobile phones, email and the like never leave us alone!

Slow Eating

It takes between 10 - 20 minutes for your brain to register that your stomach is full. We only become aware of that uncomfortably full feeling when it is much too late. So, stop eating on the run, take time to sit and enjoy your meal. This will give you time to chew and digest your food properly, allowing your stomach to send the message to your brain that you are full. Studies have shown that overweight people who slow down the pace of their eating take in fewer calories. So, by eating slowly and concentrating on your meal, you will come to eat less. You will also find that your enjoyment of the experience will increase. By relishing every mouthful you will come to appreciate fully all the flavours and textures and your food will taste so much better.

Slow Food Movement

There is a movement that originated in Italy called 'The Slow Food Movement'. The whole philosophy is just as the title suggests. Food is grown organically and just as Mother Nature intended it to be, as opposed to hurried along by the help of chemical fertilizers and hormones.

This food is then gathered and cooked in a slow manner. Meals are made from fresh ingredients and there is the absence of processed and convenience food in the diets of all 'Slow Foodies'.

The food is also eaten in a slow way. In many countries it is common practice to gather together socially and enjoy the process of eating over several hours, with the presentation of many courses. Each course is eaten in a manner that means that certain food groups are not mixed, thus preventing the digestive system from having to work harder than it needs to.

The Slow Food Movement has a lesson for us all. Of course, it is not easy just to jump out of the fast lane and slide back into the slow lane but here are some tips that will help you make this transition:

Slow Down

- Slow down. Eat like a tortoise – nice and slow. Yes, you read that correctly! Pin a picture of a tortoise on your refrigerator if this helps to remind you of your new intention.

- Say grace or show gratitude before eating – this gets you to focus on the moment.

- Stop the clock. Do not 'time' your eating. Just let your body's rhythms guide you.

- Learn to say 'no'. Your mealtime is just as important as your other commitments, so do not allow them to get in the way. Say 'no' to everything for that sacred hour.

Slow Down (continued)

- Wash your hands – watch the stress of the day disappear as you wash and mentally separate yourself from the world – make sure your environment is equipped and spacious and enjoy the act of cooking and eating.

- Let your senses guide you – smell the aroma, enjoy the colour and texture of your food and get your saliva flowing to kick start your digestion.

- Take time to relax and slow down – You may wish to try meditation, yoga or tai chi as these practices can help train both our bodies and minds to slow down.

———

Chapter 8

TIP TWO
FOLLOW NATURE'S
PRINCIPLES

> *"Understanding the laws of nature does not mean that we are immune to their operation"* ~ David Gerrold'

TIP TWO - FOLLOW NATURE'S PRINCIPLES

Mother Nature gave us the wonderful gift of life; life in a universal sense and life in the physical body sense. Externally, we experience the rising and setting of the sun, the waxing and waning of the moon and the rise and fall of the tide. If man had not invented the clock we would not have the constraints of time and would follow a much more harmonious way of living.

Today there are shops open 24 hours a day: food outlets open 24 hours, petrol stations open 24 hours and Global Financial Markets operate round the clock. In short, people are working at all hours of the day and night and we humans are naturally just not built to behave like that.

Internally we experience many biological rhythms. Women get their menstrual cycle monthly and both sexes are driven by an internal body clock that tells them when they are tired, hungry and so on. But, when we are trapped in the fast lane and following the law of man-made time patterns, we often override Mother Nature's schedule and ignore our body's rhythms.

Habits remind you of when to do the vital things such as sleeping, eating and exercising and so it is vital that you develop good routines that will ensure that you are at your physical optimum peak and protected from illness and lethargy.

Towards the end of this book we look at something called the *21 Day Challenge,* which explains how it takes just 21 days for the brain to replace one habit with a new one. Change can occur a lot sooner than you think!

Try to develop new habits that work in tune to the call of Mother Nature. Early to bed and early to rise and learn to listen to what your body is telling you. If it is hungry, then eat; if you are full, then stop eating and, when you are tired, be sure to rest. You are in control of your body, so start to treat yourself with respect.

Eat breakfast like a king, lunch like a prince, and dinner like a pauper

Routine is also important. Try to eat three meals a day, with breakfast in the morning, lunch around mid-day and dinner at sunset. This will make sure not only that you have a steady balance of energy being produced throughout the day but also that it is kept at an appropriate level for the time of day. You will want a heavier meal at mid-day so that you can have high energy levels during your working day or the daylight hours. Like Mother Nature, around mid-day the sun is at its highest and so you will be in alignment with it. In the evening, dinner should be lighter so that as the world winds down so also do you.

It is important to follow this principle, because you are driven by two clocks:

- Clock one - the natural clock. (Day and night cycle)
- Clock two - your internal body clock

Follow Nature's principles

- Get some regularity to your eating times and try to develop a pattern.
- Don't skip meals because you are busy: eat when your body needs food.
- Start the day with some warm water mixed with lemon juice to get your metabolism working.
- Try to eat food that is in season, as this works with the laws of nature.

Follow Nature's principles *(continued)*

- Don't eat too late at night as this keeps you awake. It can take up to three hours to digest food and this then gives you energy, so work with the natural rhythm of night and day and be sure to wind down in the evening.

- A breakfast, a substantial lunch and a light dinner will help you keep in tune with the ebb and flow of the 'digestive tide' and means that you are working with your biological rhythms and not against them. This digestive tide is low in the morning, peaks at lunchtime and then ebbs again in the evening.

- Early to bed and early to rise – this keeps you in flow with nature's rhythms.

Chapter 9

TIP THREE
EAT YOUR FOOD IN THE
RIGHT ENVIRONMENT

"You go to sleep in the bedroom so you should dine in the dining room" ~ *Harish Chavda*

TIP THREE - EAT YOUR FOOD IN THE RIGHT ENVIRONMENT

Our environment can play a huge role in our internal and external health. Energy is important as it can be picked up and passed on. If you are surrounded by negative energy then you will soon feel negative and drained yourself, which will then have a knock-on effect on all areas of your life and stress, depression and insomnia may plague you. Aside from these general but important issues, where you eat also influences the sort of experience that you will have in the preparation and consumption of your food.

Take time to assess your living conditions and look at what factors may be affecting your stress levels. Do you have a lot of clutter in your house? Do you exist in chaos? Your external surroundings are often a reflection of what is going on internally and vice versa. Perhaps start off by having a good clear out. You may wish to investigate the art of Feng Shui. Re-balance your surroundings for a more balanced mind, body and spirit and then set to work on correcting any imbalances that may exist within the category of eating.

Even the most beautifully prepared meal can be digested insufficiently if stress interferes with digestion. Be sure to eat your food in a space that is conducive to a relaxed and peaceful atmosphere.

Leave the hustle and bustle of everyday life outside your dining area. If and where possible, there should be no watching television whilst eating your meal, as this robs you of precious time that is better spent connecting with friends and family. Those who live in the Mediterranean area appreciate large friendly meal times and such an atmosphere is conducive to a relaxed, positive environment.

Avoid eating while working

Due to modern living in the fast lane people are spending less time eating their lunch at work than ever. For many it lasts just 15 minutes. Lunch made of sandwiches is often eaten in the office environment, sitting at a desk surfing the Internet. Eating at your desk encourages mindless eating and overeating as you are particularly likely to multi-task and not pay attention to the amount of food you are eating. This has a negative effect on your productivity and your health.

Eat your lunch away from your work environment. It is also best to take a short walk after you have eaten. This has the advantages that you will be getting exercise, fresh air and most importantly, have been able to pay 100% attention to the act of eating. When you return to work, you will be more refreshed and able to re-focus on getting things done.

Eat your food in the right environment

- Make sure that your dining table and chairs are comfortable and placed in a well-lit area. Sitting with good posture whilst eating is important, so proper upright chairs are a good idea.

- Do not eat whilst in the office or your working environment.

- Make dining an enjoyable experience by sitting down at the table with easy-listening music. You may prepare the table with a nice table cloth and candles. Relax while you eat, and make the meal pleasurable.

Eat your food in the right environment
(continued)

- Dining tables are often used as work tables or desks; you should try to keep your dining room exclusively for dining only. Keep the television and other equipment, such as the computer, out of this room as they may distract you from the process of eating.

- Eat outdoors as often as possible as this provides an alternative and beneficial environment, especially during the summer months. It allows you to connect with Mother Nature and her natural rhythms. Picnics are a relaxed way to turn mealtimes into social outings with loved ones.

- Don't eat whilst standing up or while walking because just keeping your balance uses up energy. Always be seated comfortably and allow your body to use its energy to focus on the act of eating itself.

Chapter 10

TIP FOUR
USE THE RIGHT TOOLS
FOR EATING

> **"Let your knife and fork do the work of your teeth and let your teeth do the work of your stomach."** ~ Anon

TIP FOUR - USE THE RIGHT TOOLS FOR EATING

There are no rights and wrongs when it comes to the tools that you use to eat. Practicality is more important than fashion or looks. The size of the tools: such as the knife, fork, plate or spoon is most important as this determines whether you eat the correct amount of food for your body size.

You can use a knife and fork, chopsticks or your hands, but whatever your choice of cutlery be sure that it is in good condition so that it does an adequate job. For example, make sure that your knife is sharp enough to cut the food into the correct sized pieces.

Size is important

Bigger is not necessarily better when it comes to the utensils with which you eat. In fact they may be a contributing factor to obesity. Consider this:

- The bigger the plate, the more food you can fit onto it.
- The bigger the fork or spoon, the bigger the mouthful.
- The bigger the glass, the more liquid you will drink.

Simply by reducing the size of your plate you will dramatically reduce the amount of food that you consume. Psychologically we do not register how big or small our plate is, just how much we eat and how much we leave to one side when we are finished. We are raised to 'clean our plates' of all food and often tackle a meal with this in mind.

When you go to a restaurant you are served a plate that is 'one size fits all'. But we are all unique and come in different shapes and sizes. What suits one person may not suit another and so, when you do have control of your portion size and plate size (at home), be sure to find the plate and cutlery most suited to your body size. The smaller the plate, the smaller the portion – which may well aid you to slim!

It's not just the tools you use to eat with that you need to watch for size. Be careful also which pots and pans you use to cook your food. For example, if you use an extra large saucepan then a normal portion of pasta may look as though it is inadequate when sitting at the bottom of the pan. Try not to cook too much food. Watch the size of your cooking utensils and choose a smaller saucepan.

Eating with hands

Hands are also one of the tools you can use for eating. In some Asian countries it is customary to eat all your food with your fingers, from the finest gourmet curries to simple street foods. In Western countries, however, it is considered to be ill-bred or unrefined, despite the fact that here we do eat a number of different foods with our hands. For instance, we wouldn't dream of using a knife and fork to eat our staple food, bread, nor would we chastise those who use their hands to eat meat or fish filled sandwiches and wraps, hot dogs, beef burgers, fruit, biscuits, slices of cake, pastries or ice cream cornets! Although there are certain foods that are generally seen in Western society to be completely unsuitable for eating with fingers – usually food that is covered with gravy or sauces – it is, basically, simply a matter of individual taste and culture.

One thing is sure: eating with your fingers can certainly give you a more tactile and sensual food experience.

Use the right tools for eating

- Find a plate that best suits your size; smaller is better.

- Keep food in the kitchen so that you are not tempted to go for seconds and, if you do, you have to physically get up and walk to get it. This makes you stop and think before overeating.

- Use a small spoon for dessert as this means smaller mouthfuls. You can savour the dessert better this way and eat more slowly too, which in turn aids digestion.

- Experiment with your tools and utensils, perhaps even try using chopsticks in order to prevent wolfing food down too quickly. You need to focus and be gentle.

- Practicality is more important than looks or the current fashion. Does the knife do the job? Or does it just look good?

- Try eating with your hands, as it allows you to use another sense to eat.

Chapter 11

—

TIP FIVE
DON'T LET YOUR
EMOTIONS DETERMINE
HOW YOU EAT

TIP FIVE - DON'T LET YOUR EMOTIONS DETERMINE HOW YOU EAT

Experts estimate that 75% of overeating is caused by emotional stress.

Have you ever turned to food as a way to cope with emotional feelings? It is a very common issue and most of us will do it at least once in our lives. However, for some people 'binge eating' or 'comfort eating' can be a real problem and, if left untreated, then serious health issues can result.

The key point when dealing with the relationship between food and emotions is that the trigger is emotional and therefore the mind (psychological) is controlling the body (physical). Once we tackle it from this angle it becomes clear that, if the trigger is psychological, then we can tackle it by looking at what may be the root cause of the problem. Counselling or therapy may sometimes be what is needed first, before tackling weight gain caused, for example, by binge eating.

Allowing your emotions to drive you to 'comfort eat' will result in overeating. In the long term this will cause obesity, mood swings, depression and perhaps diabetes. It is therefore a vicious cycle because the mind and body need to be balanced and to work together in order for there to be general harmony. If one or the other is out of balance then it will push the other to become unbalanced in response to it.

EXERCISE

Why not create an Art of Eating journal over a period of one month? The journal may be used to monitor what you have eaten, the times in which you ate and the way that you felt during, and after eating. You may also wish to chart your moods and emotions during each day and note down any times where you turned to food for comfort. Look at the days when this occurred and see if you can spot any triggers or patterns as, for instance, stress at work or being over tired or bored. Once you work out your triggers you can learn to control them. You can go back to the book to review techniques and tips that may help you to achieve your objective.

An example of the Art of Eating journal is shown in Figure 3

Another thing to take note of is the importance of avoiding shopping when you are emotionally upset. You will buy foods that will make you feel better and not those that are good for you.

Watching television with snacks at hand is also a bad habit. A sad film for instance will have you reaching into that bowl of popcorn or a packet of crisps and it is through such casual snacking that excess calories are absorbed without us even realizing. If you are having movie nights at home, why not cut up some celery or get some carrot sticks. This involves using your fingers and a great deal of chewing.

Objective: To lose weight				Date: 1st October 2012		
Time	Description of food	Eating Environment	Activity	How you felt while eating?	Duration	How you felt after eating?
8:00 a.m	Bowl of cereal with milk, 1 banana, glass of orange juice	Kitchen	Listening to the radio	Rushed	15 mins	Satisfied
12:30 p.m	Cheese sandwich, packet of crisps, soft drink	Office	Working on computer	Stressed	10 mins	Full
6.30 p.m	Pasta, garlic bread, salad, chocolate cake	Dining room	Watching TV	Relaxed	30 mins	Heavy

Figure 3 The Art of Eating journal

Don't let your emotions determine how you eat

- Learn the difference between physical and emotional hunger. Are you really hungry or are you looking to fill an emotional gap or stifle unwanted emotions?

- Tune into your body and treat it with respect. Nourish it and pamper it in other ways than with food. Listening to your body will address emotional issues before you find yourself turning to food as a last resort.

- You may wish to create an Art of Eating journal that monitors the relationship between food and your emotions.

- Eat slowly, and listen to your body for clues that you are satisfied.

- Don't eat mindlessly in front of the television as this may well affect your emotions (for example watching a sad film) and you will be reaching for the popcorn.

- Don't deprive yourself of foods that you love – just don't overdo it. Moderation is the key.

- Eat in the same place as often as possible because routine will enable you to change your mind-set and get into the zone that is positive and more constructive for meal-time.

- Use laughter and humour in your daily life. This will create a happy mental state.

- In case of emergency – if you do find yourself 'craving' foods for all the wrong reasons try drinking some water or take a deep breath as this will help you to refocus and calm yourself.

Chapter 12

TIP SIX
PAY FULL ATTENTION TO
THE ACT OF EATING

"Sour, sweet, bitter, pungent, all must be tasted" ~ Chinese Proverb

TIP SIX - PAY FULL ATTENTION TO THE ACT OF EATING

We were born with five senses and our Creator gave them to us for a reason. People often say: 'use it or lose it' and this saying can be applied to our senses. You know it makes sense.

Eating should be a sensory experience and not just a biological and practical function. It is not just a necessity but is also a beautiful activity, during which we can fully engage with our five senses and be as creative as our hearts desire.

Touch – your food with awareness

Taste – the food with awareness

Smell – the food with awareness

Look – at the food with awareness

Listen – to the food being eaten with awareness

Be as creative as you can be. Choose food that is rich in colour and of varied textures. Take a moment before eating to look at the food and imagine it in your mouth, savouring its aroma and imagining the delights of the eating process to come.

You should enjoy presenting your food in an exciting and interesting manner. Food is an art form that should be celebrated. Choose beautiful placemats, tablecloths, cutlery and crockery and don't be afraid to experiment with garnishes. For example, flowers are often used to garnish food in some countries. Many of the flowers in our own gardens can be used in this way such as miniature pansies or saffron flowers.

Enjoy the whole experience and, when it comes to the Art of

Eating, appreciate every mouthful as if it were your last. Imagine that you were describing your food to a person who was without every sense, apart from hearing. Tell them in as much detail as possible about the experience right from what your meal looks like to what it smells like, feels like in your mouth, tastes like and sounds like as you eat it. Be as descriptive as possible when describing your experience and use such adjectives as: meaty, tangy, sweet, spicy, peppery, hot, cold, soft, crisp, firm.

Eating with awareness

Although we continually use our five senses during day-to-day living, we often do this on autopilot. Actively engaging with your senses is something that may take a little time and practice. The trick to this is to slow down, focus on the present moment and allow yourself time in which to connect to the dish before you. Once you are thinking with clarity, you will be able to engage with your food, using your senses. Distractions will make this more difficult; so really do try to treat your dining experience in an almost sacred way.

A new concept has been introduced in France, the UK and the USA, which involves eating in a completely pitch dark restaurant. You choose your food off the menu in the lighted area and then you are led by a blind waiter to a totally dark dining room. You then use all your senses other than sight to enjoy the meal. Maybe you can try it for yourself when eating at home by using a blindfold or by closing your eyes? It will completely change the way you look at food.

Mindful Eating

Stop! Before you engage with your five senses and enjoy this experience you must ensure you clear your mind of all other thoughts and emotions.

Being mindful is to be fully engaged in the present moment. When and only when, we are connected to the present moment are we able to go with the flow of life. Many of us practice ways in which we can become more mindful and one of the most popular schools of thought on this subject is Buddhism. Linked to this is the art of meditation, which enables us physically and mentally to enter a state of deep relaxation. Once in this tranquil state we are able to connect to the present moment and exist with a clear, quiet and still mind.

Meditation is often used as a first step to another activity such as hypnosis, which prepares the mind to focus solely on one thing. Meditating before eating is a great way to mentally prepare yourself. Not only will you cut ties with the stress of the day but you will also be totally focused on the Art of Eating. Once you are in this calm and clear state you can engage your five senses and this will also keep you focused in the present moment. You are then able not only to appreciate the food that you are eating and savour every mouthful but you are also able to listen to the signals that your body is sending to you and know when you are truly satisfied.

Mindful eating is something really worth trying:

EXERCISE

1. Find something small and tasty like a grape and hold it in the palm of your hand.

2. Take a few seconds to notice your preconceived ideas of what the grape may taste like and then let go of that thought.

3. Bring your focus to the grape in your hand. Allow your senses to become alive and alert. Look at its shape and size and feel the texture of the grape. Notice the colour and feel the coolness of it on your skin.

4. Now bite into the grape and feel the burst of flavour on your tongue and teeth. As you chew, feel the texture and notice the movements of your mouth as the grape moves towards your throat and then...

5. Become aware of the absence of the grape, of its taste and aroma. Do you feel like another bite of the grape to enjoy the taste once more?

6. Now think about the way that you ate this grape and compare it to the way that you would normally just munch on a bunch of grapes. Not every munch can be classed as mindful eating.

Do you see how mindful eating in this manner gets you to focus directly on the single item? You are using all of your senses during this practice and are engaged fully with the food and with nothing else that surrounds you.

Pay full attention to the act of eating

- Pay 100% attention to the act of eating. Switch off the television, computer, radio and do not read a newspaper or book.

- Notice the presentation of things such as the layout of the table, the plates and the food itself. The creative use of candles, flowers and placemats all help to enhance the eating experience.

- Engage with your food using your five senses, so that you are connected only to the present moment and not living inside your head and thus disconnected from what is going on physically.

- Approach every mouthful with the five senses engaged and imagine you are describing the sight, texture, sound, smell and taste of each mouthful as though you were a professional food critic.

Pay full attention to the act of eating
(continued)

- Savour your food, listen to your body and, when you are satisfied, stop eating. You do not need to eat more than you desire and, remember, this is not your last meal!

- Place your fork down between mouthfuls and (when at home) try closing your eyes and truly focus on chewing and tasting what you have just put into your mouth.

Chapter 13

—

TIP SEVEN
CHEW YOUR FOOD
THOROUGHLY

"The stomach has no teeth; if your food isn't chewed in your mouth, it certainly won't be anywhere else" ~ Anon

TIP SEVEN - CHEW YOUR FOOD THOROUGHLY

A busy lifestyle often means that we are in a hurry to eat our food. But it is vital that food is chewed sufficiently for several reasons. Firstly, if you swallow bulky food you will not be able to digest it properly and will suffer with the physical pains of indigestion. Secondly, you will be missing out on vital nutrients as your digestive system cannot process the food to the best of its ability.

Another thing worth mentioning is that in the fast lane we have a tendency to veer towards ordering soft food as it is quicker to consume.

The faster that we can get it into us the better, as we all too often view eating as an annoyance or a disturbance to our busy schedule. Instead of this, try to eat foods that need to be chewed and savoured and close your eyes and focus on the Art of Chewing. This will mean that you are digesting nutrients in a better, healthier way.

The Art of Chewing

Chewing is vital. It aids digestion and slows down our eating; it also helps us to feel more satisfied with the amount of food we eat.

Chewing is sometimes referred to as mastication, which is the process by which food is crushed and ground by teeth. Chewing food begins the digestive process by breaking down the food into manageable particles and mixing it with enzymes from saliva.

Chewing food thoroughly increases the surface area of the food in the mouth and this, together with salivation, promotes the digestion of carbohydrates. It also helps to stimulate our taste buds. The more you chew the more messages your body receives about the food it is about to digest, enabling your digestive system to work more efficiently.

Living in the fast lane we often find ourselves without enough time to eat in the right way. Food is often gulped down to save time. We seem to manage to make enough time for work or even for a social life but when it comes to eating we don't make time. *We seem to live to eat not eat to live.* Eating as if it was your last meal or eating under stress will contribute to a reduction in the number of times food in the mouth is chewed.

How many times should you chew your food?

The number of times you chew will depend on the type of food you are eating. Soft foods such as fruit and soft vegetables break down more easily than harder foods such as steak or chicken, so you will chew a different amount of times for various foods. Some experts suggest that foods should be chewed 10 to 40 times before swallowing. In any case, the main point to bear in mind is that you should make sure the food in your mouth has reached the consistency of soup before swallowing.

It may take some time for you to master all the practices outlined and you will almost certainly find yourself spending much longer over your meals and, as a result, you will find that you are appreciating your food much better. And it may even help you to control your weight.

Chewing and weight connection

According to results published in the *American Journal of Clinical Nutrition*, chewing thoroughly may help control weight. Chewing food 40 times caused study participants to eat nearly 12 percent fewer calories. People who chew their food more take in fewer calories.

Chew your food thoroughly

- Eat slowly. Allow yourself enough time for your meal so that you can eat in a relaxed and leisurely fashion.

- Avoid wolfing down your food. Savour the food you're consuming.

- Eat food in smaller morsels

- Cut your food into bite sized pieces at a time, because too much food in your mouth at any time makes it more difficult to chew the food thoroughly.

- Chew in such a manner that the food is the consistency of soup when it is finally swallowed.

- While you are chewing your food, put your cutlery down and don't pick it up again until you have fully chewed and swallowed the last mouthful. Also do not have food on your fork or spoon until the previous mouthful has been thoroughly chewed and swallowed.

- Wait until you have completely finished chewing and swallowing before taking another bite. Gulping down food or swallowing too quickly can cause choking or digestive problems.

Chapter 14

TIP EIGHT
EAT THE RIGHT
AMOUNT OF FOOD

TIP EIGHT - EAT THE RIGHT AMOUNT OF FOOD

Portion control is something to which we should all pay more attention. Life in the fast lane can lead to us not paying full attention to what we serve on our plate and this can lead to illness and obesity. It can also lead to snacking throughout the day rather than sticking to the habit of three meals a day and this can mean that we are not fully aware of the amount of food that we are digesting in any one day.

Getting into the routine of three meals a day and using tools and utensils most suited to your body size will mean that you are aware of what you are eating. Try to imagine your plate is divided into segments and fill it with plenty of vegetables or salad and go easy on the carbohydrates. Be sure to have a balance of all food groups and don't just load your plate with one particular favourite.

As mentioned previously, be sure to use pots and pans that are smaller in size. Often we cook too much food because we use a pan that is too large and this is how we wind up with the temptation to pile more onto our plates and go back for seconds.

Waste not, want not?

If you are full and you leave some food on the plate, do not feel guilty. The idea that we have to clear the plate and not waste anything is why a lot of us continue to eat even when our bodies have given us the signals that it has had more than enough. If you are at home, perhaps the uneaten food could be carefully placed in plastic containers and stored in the fridge for another day. Far too much food is thrown away these days wastefully and unnecessarily.

The snacking habit

One bad habit to make a mental note of to avoid at this point is compulsive snacking. This is what can lead to a rise in our daily intake of food. Watching how much we eat and what we eat at mealtimes will enable us to be aware of how much we are consuming. However, many of us forget, when doing our daily count up, to add on those little bits of 'in-between foods' we tend to eat and that can be where those extra pounds are coming from!

We tend to feel guilty about treating ourselves to that 'naughty but nice' sweet delicacy. One way to tackle this issue is to rid yourself of this guilt and understand that the odd treat now and then is actually good for you. Work it into mealtimes such as a nice dessert every so often, and savour the pleasure rather than shovelling it down guiltily.

Small but frequent snacks of things such as crisps and chocolates can give rise to conditions such as acne, gas, diabetes, tooth decay, obesity, and a sluggish digestive system. If you really must snack then try to replace these items with healthier options such as celery sticks, carrots or fruit.

However, it is so important to remember that you do need to eat. Starving yourself is just as bad as overeating. The key to optimum health is the right food in the right proportions at the right time.

You might not immediately think that you are an under-eater but many people are just that, without being aware of it. When people are stressed and emotional they tend to go one of two ways. Either they comfort eat and consume more than they need or they lose their appetite and under eat and so deplete the body's energy even further. Anytime you are feeling stressed, think about it like revving the engine of a car. The harder you rev the more fuel it uses so, while obviously taking steps to de-stress yourself, make sure your tank is topped up with enough good nutritious fuel to give you all the energy you need.

Getting the balance right

Like most things in nature, striking the right balance is the key to wellbeing. We have known this for centuries; even Aristotle described it as the desirable middle between the extremes of excess and deficiency (overeating and not eating enough), the 'golden mean'.

Portion Control

Portion control is eating a healthy balance of amounts and types of varied foods. As highlighted earlier, either too much or too little of the same thing can be bad for you. Just as your food choices make a huge difference, so too do the size of your portions. If you are concerned that you may be eating too much, simply try using a smaller plate and, in doing so, give your brain the illusion of eating more. You will be surprised how effective it is. But, above all, slow down, sit back, relax and listen to your body. It'll tell you everything you need to know.

Eat the right amount of food

- Don't overfill your plate because you can always go back for seconds.

- Eat slowly and steadily so that your body can alert you when you are full.

- Divide your plate into sections and be sure to have a healthy balance of food groups.

Eat the right amount of food *(continued)*

- Keep second helpings out of sight and out of mind. If you have them on the table you will be more likely to dip in for more. Keep seconds in the kitchen so that you have to get up to go and fetch them.

- Remember to use plates and utensils that are smaller than those you usually use. This will fool your eye into thinking that you have more on the plate.

- Rule of thumb – eat what you can hold in the palm of your hands - *Ayurveda* says that one should eat only the amount of food that fits in both hands when held together.

- Divide one meal into courses – you may have salad and carbohydrates as a starter and meat as a course separately, so as not to mix all the food groups together at once. This can help stage the meal – and slow the whole process down a little.

- Try not to keep snacks in your home. You will be less inclined to use them if you have to get up off your sofa and walk to the local store to get them!

- When eating at a restaurant make sure you ask the waiter the size of portions and then order the meal accordingly. Once you have ordered the food and you can't eat it all, don't be afraid to leave some on the plate.

Chapter 15

TIP NINE
BOOST YOUR DIGESTION

> *"Do not worry, eat three square meals a day, say your prayers, be courteous to your creditors, keep your digestion good, exercise, go slow and easy"* ~ Abraham Lincoln

TIP NINE - BOOST YOUR DIGESTION

When you eat foods such as bread, meat and vegetables, they are not in a form that the body can use as nourishment straightaway. Digestion is the process by which food and drink are broken down into their smallest parts so the body can use them to build and nourish cells and to provide energy. If this process is not carried out efficiently then you will not get the full benefits of the food you eat. No matter how *nutritious* the food is, or how you eat your food, your body must also correctly process it, absorb nutrients and eliminate waste for peak health.

Factors such as stress, lack of sleep, antibiotics, illness, aging, and poor diet choices can lead to digestive problems. Toxins can also build up in our body, which, in turn, can speed the aging process and play a role in causing degenerative diseases. Symptoms of poor digestion include: bloating, flatulence (gas), diarrhoea, constipation and fatigue.

How to boost your digestion

Here are some specific things that you can do to boost your digestion. Remember, everyone is different and has a different body type. What follows is only a guide.

Drinking liquids

Drinking water is good for you. General advice suggests we should drink between one and three litres of liquid per day. This does not need to be in the form of water although water is best.

Drinking warm water with a dash of lemon first thing in the morning will help to kick- start the waste elimination process. Avoid iced drinks and cold food as food is more efficiently digested at body temperature, and therefore cold fluids or food can slow down the digestive processes. If you must drink while eating take liquids at room temperature. Herbal teas such as mint or chamomile can be very beneficial as they aid digestion.

Eating fibre rich foods

Eating fibre-rich food can benefit your health in many ways as it aids the body with good bowel movements, lowers blood-cholesterol levels and improves blood glucose levels. Your diet should preferably contain fresh fruit, vegetables, brown rice, seeds, nuts, wholemeal pasta and bread. It is best to eat home cooked food rather than convenience foods as it is better for your health and will also save you money.!

Daily exercise

Regular physical activity such as brisk walking or jogging can aid the body to detox naturally and also help the elimination process. At least a half hour of daily exercise and stretching will improve blood circulation and also burn calories.

Fresh juice

Drinking fresh fruit or vegetable juice is one of the very best gifts that you can give to your body. Freshly juiced vegetables will give your body an instant boost of nutrients, enzymes, vitamins and minerals in a form that the body can easily assimilate, absorb and digest. Perhaps you might like to try different combination of juices such as carrot, cucumber, celery, spinach, cabbage, beetroot, apple, orange, pear and grapes.

Drinking Aloe Vera can also be beneficial as it aids digestion and cleanses the body.

Herbs, spices and bitter food

Adding more herbs, spices and bitter food to your diet may help improve your digestion. Herbs and spices have been used for cooking since ancient times. They also add flavour and improve the taste of your food. Spices and herbs that are known to be beneficial include the following:

Spices: Ginger, black pepper, mustard, cumin, cinnamon, cayenne, caraway seeds, cardamom, cloves, turmeric.

Herbs: Oregano, parsley, sage, coriander, rosemary, basil, thyme, mint.

Bitter foods: Chicory, watercress, broccoli, spinach, asparagus, cabbage, horseradish.

Triphala the wonder herb

Triphala is an Ayurvedic herbal formula which consists of equal parts of three fruits: Amalaki, Bibhitaki and Haritaki. Triphala was formulated by Ayurvedic physicians thousands of years ago in India. It is an all round natural tonic used to improve digestive functions. Triphala is available in a powder, capsule and tablet form.

Fasting

Short-term fasting is one way to allow the digestive system a well deserved break and it helps eliminate toxins. Remember always to drink plenty of fruit and vegetable juice during your fast. Also plan your fasting for days when you will not be doing lots of hard physical work and can take plenty of rest. You will find that you have a better appreciation of your food after fasting.

After a meal

For some people it may well be a good idea to take a gentle walk after eating. In many countries it has been long known that a walk is one of the greatest aids in digesting food properly. Walking is one of the most natural forms of exercise and its gentle, low impact is extremely valuable to overall health and well being. As you walk your body will receive more oxygen, your mind will get a rest from the work-a-day routine and your digestive system will benefit from the movement.

Boost your digestion

- Drink more liquids and fresh juice.

- Chewing is one of the most important mechanisms of digestion, so chew, chew, chew your food!

- Use herbs and spices to boost your digestion and enhance the flavour of your food.

- Give your digestive system a rest – try fasting.

- Eat regular smaller meals.

- Take smaller bites of food when eating.

- Go for a leisurely stroll after a meal as it is good for your digestion.

Chapter 16

TIP TEN
RELAX AFTER EATING

"Your mind will answer most questions if you learn to relax and wait for the answer." ~ *William S. Burroughs*

TIP TEN - RELAX AFTER EATING

Did you know that digestion takes up quite a bit of energy? So, when you have finished eating, don't be in a rush to get out there and 'burn those calories off'. Your body will do a good job of that for you on its own.

Give your body time to digest what you have eaten and avoid strenuous activities such as swimming or running immediately after a meal. After a little rest this is a great way to put your energy to good use but allow at least two hours to pass before you do so.

Think of a banquet: once the guests have finished eating do they jump up and head off to do something strenuous? No. It is traditional that speeches are made and the guests sit around to chat with their neighbours. An after dinner chat or word of gratitude is something that you could add to your daily routine as it helps you to wind down before getting up from the table right away.

Whatever you decide to do you need to be constantly aware that, if you interfere with your body's digestion period, then all of the hard work that you put into the art of eating will have been for nothing.

Relax after eating

- Sit quietly for a few minutes after eating.

- Avoid doing strenuous exercise for at least two hours after eating.

- Do not have a bath or shower immediately after eating as this will weaken the digestive system around the stomach area.

- After dinner liquor can also help with digestion and relaxation.

- Herbal teas such as peppermint, fennel or chamomile are a nice way to round off a meal.

- A tradition such as an after dinner speech or a simple chat with your host or dinner companion can allow time for a breather directly after eating and keep everyone seated and relaxed.

- Activities such as watching television or sitting reading the newspaper are ideal ways of relaxing.

- Avoid going to sleep immediately after eating. Your digestion slows down when you lie down to go to sleep.

- Relax! Leave the washing up until later – your health is more important.

Chapter 17

THE RESULTS AND BENEFITS

THE RESULTS AND BENEFITS

If you want to journey forward to good health, you will be well on the way if you follow the guidelines in this book. The key points to think about when following this journey to health are:

- Be open to new ideas and try to get your friends and family involved too? Support is always encouraging and meal times are more enjoyable when shared with loved ones.

- Remember that everyone is different and what works for one person may not work for another. Don't compare yourself to others, just focus on your own journey.

The benefits of learning the Art of Eating

If you have paid attention to the techniques taught within the pages of this book and if you practice all the tips that you have been given, you will very quickly begin to reap the amazing benefits. Some of these benefits include:

1. Enhanced communication with your mind and body – your mind will tell you what foods are bad for it, what it does and doesn't need and you will learn how to listen and respond to it.

2. You will appreciate and enjoy food far better than ever before.

3. You will feel happier, more content, more relaxed and healthy, as your body adjusts to a better diet and an increase in nutrients.

4. You will finally free yourself from the stressful experience that is life in the fast lane.

5. You will develop a sense of immediacy – you will learn how to focus on the present moment. This advice is not just restricted to food and eating, it will enhance all areas of your life.

Physical benefits include:

1. You will be able to manage your ideal weight.

2. Any ailments you may have been experiencing will begin to clear up and good health will be restored.

3. Energy levels will rocket up and you will be far more efficient than you ever imagined.

4. Skin, hair, and nails will improve and you will find yourself feeling more physically attractive than ever before.

5. Your immune system will function at its optimum. General sickness will be decreased as you are better protected.

6. Live longer! Yes, your life expectancy will increase with your new way of living and eating, so expect to increase your life expectancy by some years.

Psychological benefits include:

1. Less general stress and anxiety as you learn to slow down and focus on the present moment.

2. An increased awareness of the role that emotional fluctuations play in your eating habits, your new lifestyle can lead to a greater awareness of mood fluctuations, which you can learn to control by looking at your personal 'triggers'.

3. A deeper sense of general relaxation.

4. An improved sense of balance of the mind, body and spirit.

5. Improved self esteem and self-confidence as skin, hair, nails and so forth begin to glow with vitality.

I hope that the journey through this book has proved liberating and enjoyable for you and that, although the concept is simple, it has perhaps proved to be the missing link to all that you have tried so far.

Once you have addressed the issue of how to eat, you can then work on other areas, such as particular diets, safe in the knowledge that, when you combine the "how to" with the "what to" in the world of eating, then you are better prepared than ever before. I can promise you that the results will simply astound you.

Here's to a new and revitalized YOU!

APPENDIX ONE

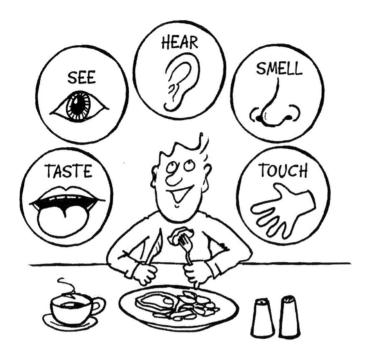

How to eat correctly – The Seven Steps

Step One: Look at the food *(Sight)*

Step Two: Smell the aroma of the food *(Smell)*

Step Three: Feel the food in your mouth *(Touch / Feel)*

Step Four: Taste the food in your mouth *(Taste)*

Step Five: Notice the sound the food makes as you chew *(Sound)*

Step Six: Swallow the food

Step Seven: Relax and take deep breath

Repeat the cycle again, going back to Step One.

APPENDIX TWO

Ten Healthy Eating Tips

Tip 1 - Slow down and eat like a tortoise! Nice and Slow!

Tip 2 - Follow Nature's Principles

Tip 3 - Eat your food in the right environment

Tip 4 - Use the right tools for eating

Tip 5 - Don't let your emotions determine how you eat

Tip 6 - Pay full attention to the act of eating

Tip 7 - Chew your food thoroughly

Tip 8 - Eat the right amount of food

Tip 9 - Boost your digestion

Tip 10 - Relax after eating

ACKNOWLEDGEMENTS

First and foremost I would like to dedicate this book to my father, mother and sister.

Second, I would like to thank my wife Usha for standing beside me throughout my career and writing this book. I would also like to thank my wonderful children Rajesh, Jenny, Deepa, Jaimini, Nikhil and my sister Manjula for supporting me in writing this book.

It is with great honour that I acknowledge my mentors, teachers, friends, editors:

Tony Robbins (life coach), Dr Deepak Chopra, Eckhart Tolle, Napoleon Hill, BEHT Yoga Group, Nick Williams, Dr Madan Kataria

Ali Campbell (Mr Fix It), Richard Duszczak (Cartoons), Arvind Devalia, Jo Parfitt, David Ashford, John Monaghan.

Special thanks to Narendra Gohil for his constant guidance, encouragement and support.

To my friends who attended my first Art of Eating seminar - Denis Lobo, Pravin Soma, Satish Kainth, Rajendra Nanavati, Darshan Gill, Navin Rathod and Vinod Gadhvana.

I take this opportunity to express my gratitude to following people who have helped with the book project: David Backham, Alex Farrugia, Ashok, Hiren and Nikhil Shah, Helen Spark, Gerry Bloomfield, Rowena Desouza, Lakvinder Singh, Sue Thomas, Mukesh and Milesh Nanavati.

Finally I would also like to thank everyone who attended my seminars for their contributions and feedback.

WEBSITE AND FURTHER INFORMATION

Educational seminars and workshops

I run educational seminars and workshops on health and stress-free living. Workshops are held regularly for groups, organisations and individuals.

Laughter Therapy

Laughter yoga is fun to do and has a number of health benefits including stress relief and boosting the immune system. Laughter yoga therapy sessions can be tailored to individuals or groups.

Massage Therapy

Indian head massage helps to relieve stress, tension, fatigue, insomnia, headaches, migraine and sinusitis. A typical treatment session includes a 15 minute consultation followed by the head massage which normally lasts 45 minutes.

Life Coaching

Has your doctor ever recommended a lifestyle change that you couldn't keep up for long? Have you ever wanted something in your life, but found you couldn't achieve it alone? I can help you! I work with you to provide ongoing support and guidance as you set goals and make long term changes that improve your health and happiness.

If you have been inspired by this book and would like more information about the services I offer and other useful resources visit:

Website: **www.artofeating.co.uk**

Email: **info@artofeating.co.uk**